Institute

# Maritime Security handbook:
## coping with piracy

by

**Steven Jones** MSc BSc (Hons) MNI

# Maritime Security handbook:
## coping with piracy

by

### Steven Jones MSc BSc (Hons) MNI

Steven Jones has asserted his right under the Copyright, Designs and
Patents Act 1988 to be identified as the author of this book

**Published by The Nautical Institute**

202 Lambeth Road, London SE1 7LQ, England

Tel: +44 (0)20 7928 1351     Fax: +44 (0)20 7401 2817     Web: www.nautinst.org

© The Nautical Institute 2013

This handbook has been published as part of The Nautical Institute's maritime security suite and as a companion volume to *Maritime Security: a practical guide*, second edition, 2012 by the same author.

This book has been prepared to address the subject of coping with piracy. This should not, however, be taken to mean that this document deals comprehensively with all of the concerns that will need to be addressed, or even, when a particular need is addressed, that this document sets out the only definitive view for all situations. The opinions expressed are those of the author only and are not necessarily to be taken as the policies or views of any organisation with which he has any connection.

Book Editor Margaret Freeth
Cover image: The Security Association for the Maritime Industry (SAMI)
Typesetting and layout by Phil McAllister – PMD Visual Communications
Printed in England by Geerings Print Ltd
**ISBN 978 1 906915 46 9**

# Acknowledgements

Numerous people and organisations helped in the production of this book, providing well-placed advice, guidance and expertise. In particular I would like to thank the following, as the book would not have been possible without their efforts, support, and assistance. Thank you:

**Dr Phil Anderson FNI**, ConsultISM Ltd

**Stephen Askins**, Ince and Co

**Captain Thomas Brown**, Seacurus Ltd

**Peter Cook**, Security Association for the Maritime Industry (SAMI)

**Ray Gibbons**, Sentinel Maritime Ltd

**Bridget Hogan** and **Margaret Freeth**, The Nautical Institute

**The International Transport Intermediaries Club (ITIC)**

**Adrian King**, Allen Vanguard Ltd

**Howard Leedham MBE**, STL Maritime Ltd

**Dr James A Malcolm**, Coventry University

**Gianna Molica-Franco**, Seren Creative Ltd

**Captain Stuart Nicholls**, Stratum Five Ltd

**Julian Parker FNI OBE**

**Anneley Pickles**, Shiptalk Ltd

**Michael Williams**, MIRIS International Ltd

**Roy Winfield**

# Foreword

by **Captain P Mukundan**

Director,
ICC International Maritime Bureau

Recent attacks against ships off the Horn of Africa and the Gulf of Guinea have renewed attention on the effects of piracy and armed robbery, particularly upon the crew. For the first time in many decades, the tragic consequences to crew who are held for long months and even years in pirate captivity have been highlighted.

While there are commercial solutions to most losses arising from these incidents there is no way to adequately compensate crew for the trauma that many go through.

Can these incidents be avoided? Can crew be better prepared for the unfamiliar circumstances they face when their vessel is hijacked or they are violently attacked?

One way to improve their preparation is to make them aware of the risks and types of attacks which take place in the world's key high risk areas. This will help to reduce anxiety and hopefully result in them making better decisions – firstly by understanding the true nature of the threat, and secondly in acting in a manner that significantly reduces tensions on board once the vessel has been boarded by pirates.

Crew in most other forms of transport, such as aviation, are frequently drilled in such emergencies but it is only in the light of recent piracy incidents that the shipping industry is beginning to tackle this important information deficit.

To be effective, such advice should be factual and objective.

This book by Steven Jones provides a contemporaneous review of the threat of attack in different sea areas, practical actions which can be taken by Masters and crew to minimise the risk of an attack succeeding, and sound advice on what can be done to protect the crew should the vessel be boarded.

It fills an important need.

*Dedicated to all seafarers who have suffered from the pain and fear of piracy, and for those who are tragically still being held hostage today.*

# Contents

# Introduction

Most experts agree that in the long term the war against piracy will be won ashore, but in the meantime the battles are taking place out at sea. This brings with it unique challenges to protect vessels, provide training and deliver a stream of useable and timely intelligence and data.

While we accept the real answer to piracy is such positive action and engagement, in the short term shipping has to be protected. Key to this is the adoption and implementation of the Best Management Practices (BMP) for both Somali-based piracy and its West African iteration. However, it is currently felt that adherence to BMP may be patchy and in some cases non-existent.

The guidance within the BMP is a route map to hardening the vessel. It is not about selecting some of the guidance or addressing individual elements – it is all or nothing. The advice is simple and clear – implement the guidance and the vessel has a chance, but ignore it and the likelihood of being hijacked increases. Far too many vessels, for various reasons, are failing in their duty to protect themselves and are leaving crews vulnerable.

Whether through ignorance or negligence, some operators and crews are taking a Russian roulette approach that places seafarers and the responding armed forces at risk. There have been positive changes, but there are still weaknesses and failings. There can be no excuses and all vessel operators in the high risk area have to be ready to respond and react to pirate attacks. Unfortunately the advice within the BMP is seen by many as a hassle that takes up valuable time and resources. However, the measures recommended are the minimum and are not up for debate.

While there have been some successes against pirates it is clear that a stronger hand is needed in both guiding and enforcing compliance with BMP. There are lessons from some flag states, with the US leading the way in applying stringent standards and measures for its own flagged and owned vessels. Now is the time for others to follow suit. Anything less than the best management practices is simply not good enough.

BMP is available to download or purchase in hard copy form. See www.mschoa.org for full details.

## Maritime Security handbook

Away from the actions which can be taken at sea, we must remember that piracy is killing seafarers and destroying lives and livelihoods. Despite some recent successes in combating it, there is no acceptable level of piracy.

This handbook forms part of The Nautical Institute's maritime security suite and should be used in conjunction with the main volume covering principles and practice (Steven Jones, *Maritime Security: a practical guide*, second edition published 2012) and the handbooks on stowaways and crime (in preparation). Piracy is one of the threats that must be assessed and planned for in the Ship Security Plan (SSP) and in the provision of training and equipment to ensure that crew members can protect themselves and their vessel and take whatever action is necessary.

**Steven Jones MSc BSc (Hons) MNI**
*September 2013*

# Chapter 1

## Introduction to piracy

### KEY ADVICE

- Understanding what piracy is in legal and practical terms
- Appreciating the importance of reporting attacks
- Understanding the commercial implications

Piracy is an ancient and established threat to ships, people and cargoes and re-emerges whenever and wherever the circumstances are attractive. Over the past 30 years we have found ourselves in the grip of a modern piracy epidemic, with a form of piracy that has evolved into a faster, more ruthless, organised and violent threat than ever before.

Modern piracy is violent, bloody and ruthless and is made all the more fearsome because its victims know they are alone and defenceless. Seafarers have a basic human right to expect to sail on safe ships in safe waters and no one ashore can fully appreciate the trauma these types of attacks can cause, both physically and mentally.

The main aim of piracy can vary, depending on where it occurs and by whom it is perpetrated. Theft of cash and valuables, particularly from the Master's safe, is often involved but all kinds of ship's stores have been taken, including the contents of upper deck lockers and stores. In some cases whole ships have been stolen, their cargo taken and their crew murdered and the ship subsequently sold.

According to the London-based International Maritime Bureau (IMB), there has been a rising wave of piracy from 2005 onward, with vessels and crews hijacked off the coast of Somalia. The numbers fluctuate but thankfully it seems that for the first time in a number of years the hitherto increasing frequency and ferocity of attacks is finally diminishing. However, there are now concerns that complacency could set in – and this should be avoided as the Somali pirate problem is not ended yet.

Piracy is not limited to the Indian Ocean, as the traditional piracy area of Asia remains a live concern and the Gulf of Guinea and parts of West Africa are experiencing heightened pirate activity.

The Regional Cooperation Agreement on Combating Piracy and Armed Robbery against Ships in Asia (ReCAAP) has reported rises across Asia, but this has been largely due to an increase in incidents in ports and anchorages.

New piracy hotspots open up and old ones can flare again. Shipowners are urged to closely monitor the security situation in areas into which they trade or transit.

Littoral states with a coastline in a particular area have legal responsibilities to ensure the freedom of innocent passage but in the main piracy is seen as a crime against foreign crews, ships and cargo. In many cases it is not viewed as a major concern.

The reality is that piracy is a global problem, affecting all shipping nations. The IMB has stated that attacks on ships with controlling interests in the US and European Union have accounted for around 37% of attacks over the past two years.

There are massive cost implications to consider. An estimate was produced by the One Earth Future Foundation in its *Oceans Beyond Piracy* study that the overall cost of paying ransoms and insurance premiums, costs of re-routeing ships, purchasing security equipment and providing naval forces totals $7-12Bn annually.

## What is piracy?

A definition of piracy was laid down in the 1958 Geneva Convention on the High Seas (Article 15), which also makes up Article 101 of the United Nations Convention on the Law of the Sea (UNCLOS) 1982 and declares piracy a criminal act.

The definition can be found in the Nautical Institute publication already cited (Steven Jones, *Maritime Security: a practical guide*, second edition published 2012), but put simply, attacks inside territorial water are not piracy while those outside are. Restricting piracy to the high seas means that an alternative term has to be created for attacks against ships within territorial waters.

The territorial sea is a belt of water not exceeding 12 miles in width measured from the territorial sea baseline (TSB). The term TSB refers to the line from which the seaward limits of the state's maritime zones are measured. In its most basic terms it relates to the low water line along the coast.

A state's sovereignty extends to the territorial sea, its seabed and subsoil, and to the air space above it. This sovereignty is exercised in accordance with international law as reflected in UNCLOS. The major limitation on the state's exercise of sovereignty in the territorial sea is the right of innocent passage for foreign ships.

Beyond the territorial limits are the "high seas" or "international waters" – this is where the legal concept of piracy applies.

The industry Best Management Practices (BMP), state that a piracy attack may include (but is not limited to) actions such as:

- Use of violence against the ship or its personnel, or any attempt to use violence
- Attempt(s) to board the vessel where the Master suspects the persons are pirates
- An actual boarding, whether successful in gaining control of the vessel or not
- Attempts to overcome the ship's self-protection measures by use of ladders, grappling hooks or weapons deliberately used against or at the vessel

The BMP distinguish between four different levels of pirate activity – pirate attack, hijack, illegal boarding and suspicious or aggressive approach.

A **pirate attack**, as opposed to an approach, is where a vessel has been subjected to an aggressive approach by a pirate craft AND weapons have been discharged.

A **hijack** is where pirates have boarded and taken control of a vessel against the crew's will.

An **illegal boarding** is where pirates have boarded a vessel but have not taken control. Command remains with the Master. The most obvious example of this is the citadel scenario.

Action taken by another craft may be deemed **suspicious** if any of the following occur (the list is not exhaustive):

- A definite course alteration towards the craft associated with a rapid increase in speed by the suspected craft, which cannot be accounted for as normal activity in the circumstances prevailing in the area
- Small craft sailing on the same course and speed for an uncommon period and distance, not in keeping with normal fishing or other circumstances prevailing in the area

- Sudden changes in course towards the vessel and aggressive behaviour

In helping to evaluate suspicious activity, BMP state that the following may be of assistance to determine the nature of a suspect vessel:

- Number of crew on board relative to its size
- Closest point of approach (CPA)
- Unusual and non-fishing equipment, such as ladders, climbing hooks or large amounts of fuel, on board
- Armed in excess of the level commonly experienced in the area
- Weapons fired in the air

Other events, activity and craft may be deemed suspicious by the Master. Much is left to the experienced assessment of the Master.

## Piracy reporting

The IMB's Piracy Reporting Centre (PRC) is the only independent centre of its kind in the world. It offers ships and their crews a facility to report pirate attacks at any time and can also provide assistance anywhere in the world via a single point of contact.

In order to establish a better picture of the problem of piracy and armed robbery, the IMB encourages the reporting of more attacks and attempted attacks to the PRC, whose role extends far beyond compiling reports and issuing warnings.

The work of the PRC is funded by 22 organisations including P&I clubs, shipowners and insurers. In addition to documenting the facts, the IMB's annual report on piracy and armed robbery assesses developments in pirate activity and identifies piracy-prone areas so that ships can take preventive action.

The IMB believes that a large number of attacks remain unreported and more incidents may well come to light in the future. It is thought that official reports account for only 50% of attacks, as shipowners fear that if they report an incident their ship will be detained for an inquiry, which could result in further financial losses. Spending a week in port could cost more in lost time than the amount lost during the pirate attack. Unless there is a murder or a vessel seizure the act of piracy may go unreported.

Many shipping companies also fear the adverse publicity that will ensue and possible increases in insurance costs associated with trading in pirate black spot regions. Under-reporting is particularly problematic in Asia. Although the attitude "that nothing will be done, so there is no point in reporting" is perhaps understandable, it must be guarded against.

Over a number of years Andrew Robinson of the marine security consultancy IMS has recorded maritime security incidents globally which exceed those collected by official agencies. This is a concern, as it seems we are not reporting or recording data properly. He commented: "If we cannot count or record attacks effectively we are underestimating the threat posed by piracy and the statistics produced will perhaps underplay the problem, lessening the political response." Robinson's methodology is to include all security incidents and then divide them into appropriate categories. This ties in with the BMP approach.

According to the BMP, harmonising common definitions for piracy attacks and suspicious activity will ensure:

- Harmonised data assessment
- Provision of consistent reporting
- Harmonised intelligence gathering
- Better accuracy in assessing the efficiency of (naval) counter-piracy operations and BMP effectiveness, as well as defining future end-dates to operations

# Chapter 2
## Types of piracy

**KEY ADVICE**

- Understanding the conditions in which piracy develops
- Assessing problem areas and piracy hotspots
- Understanding different types of pirate attack
- Implementing basic precautions

## Conditions driving piracy

There are certain conditions which are believed to act as a potential catalyst driving piracy. Where crew, vessels and cargoes pass through (or near) coastal areas or states which are in conflict, which are unstable and which experience harsh economic conditions, shipping is likely to be a tempting target.

Many seafarers are familiar with the concept of the fire triangle in which heat, fuel and oxygen are all necessary to support combustion. The piracy triangle theory works in the same way. If one or more of the three drivers listed above are removed, then piracy will be reduced or may disappear completely.

**Figure 1 The piracy triangle theory**

When looking at the patterns of modern piracy attacks, the vast majority take place in the tropical zone, between the Tropics of Cancer and Capricorn. It would appear that three main factors lead to, and subsequently drive, piracy in any particular region:

### Instability

Areas which suffer from political, social or religious instability tend to be a breeding ground for piracy. Instability often turns to armed conflict, which in turn can drive criminal activity. Where the rule of law is weak or the apparatus to enforce it is the subject of conflict, then again piracy is a likely outcome.

Wars and conflict often appear to lead to piracy – disputes between Aceh rebels in Indonesia, the problems in war-torn Somali, terrorism in Nigeria and the Philippines have all lead to outbreaks of piracy. In the past, the conflicts in Vietnam and Cambodia led to increased criminality out at sea.

### Complexity

Areas which are geographically or territorially complex can support piracy. Such conditions may allow pirates to conceal their whereabouts or allow them to move between jurisdictions to avoid capture and prosecution. While modern surveillance capabilities (satellite, drones, etc) have led to a drop off in the concealment of stolen vessels, territorial complexity is significant. Areas with multiple territorial waters can hamper the pursuit and capture of pirates, and so can facilitate piracy.

As piracy off Somalia took hold, it was the inability of the military to enter the territorial waters which was seen as a major problem in tackling it. Similar issues are also emerging off West Africa, as pirates escape into their own waters. For a long time in the Malacca Strait the fact that pirates could move between the waters of Malaysia, Singapore and Indonesia meant they could evade capture.

### Economic disparity

In areas of poverty the temptation to plunder vessels can be strong. Locals are more susceptible to the overtures of organised crime, and are often tempted into illegal activities.

Many leading security analysts see the main reasons for the increasing number of attacks in Asian and African waters as economic. Pirates are often local people who try to supplement their income or take advantage of the lapses in security which economic issues may force.

Pirates have increasingly plagued the waters around Indonesia, due to deteriorating economic and social conditions. These conditions result in part from internal security problems but are also heightened by natural disasters.

Historically, regions blighted by poverty have long been pirate hotspots and the downturn over recent years in the economic progress of many Asian nations has meant financial ruin for many people. Their anger, resentment and financial concerns have sparked a boom in illegal activities.

Many small-scale pirate gangs operating today seem to fit this pattern, as piracy can be thought of as a form of 'cottage industry' in areas of Indonesia and the Philippines where agrarian and fishing pursuits alone may be insufficient to support the local village economy. Many pirates have 'day jobs' as legitimate fishermen or traders but supplement their income with piracy – but only when the ships are easy targets.

The rewards for pirates must outweigh the risks. Pirates want and need areas where it is possible to avoid detection and which provide safe havens. Once the stakes are raised all but the most committed, desperate or greedy pirates will revert back to their other lines of business.

The cruel irony of piracy is that it is most prevalent in nations least equipped to deal with the problem. The political, geographic and economic reasons described above conspire to give us piracy in southeast Asia, off the Indian Subcontinent, the Horn of Africa and West Africa and in parts of the Caribbean.

## Somalia/Gulf of Aden/Indian Ocean

Piracy, and more especially the hijacking of ships and the taking of crews for ransom, has reached unprecedented levels in and around the waters of Somalia, the Gulf of Aden, Red Sea and Indian Ocean over recent years.

This has been despite the introduction of ISPS Code procedures and measures, indicating the need for shipboard personnel to rethink and re-focus their security mindset, vigilance and actions when operating in or near areas that suffer from piracy.

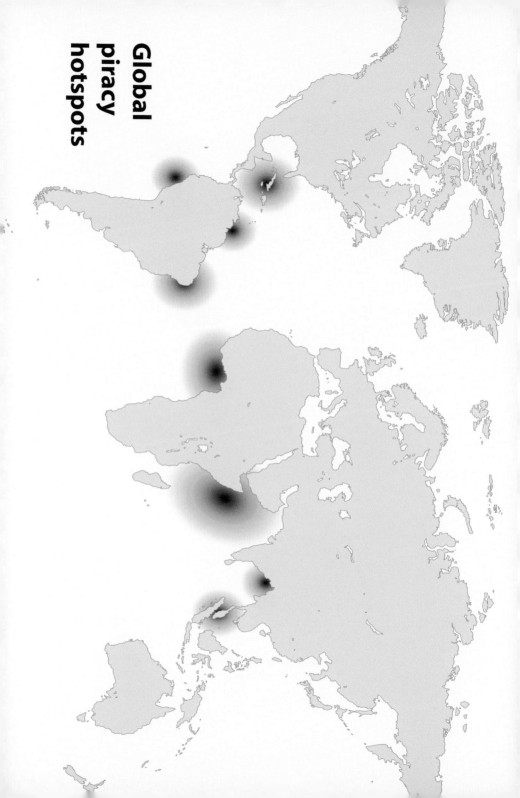

# Global piracy hotspots

The advent of piracy in this particular area has meant that it is necessary to develop and provide guidance to be followed before, during and after attack, and in the event of kidnapping of personnel.

The waters off Somalia and the Gulf of Aden have become a hunting ground for pirate gangs looking to board vessels. This is not simply a coastal zone problem, nor is it limited to territorial waters – vessels are being attacked far out to sea and measures should be taken even when hundreds of miles off the coast. Some attacks are launched from shore bases but as the targets have moved offshore, so too have the pirates. They now often use mother ships to launch attacks, with these vessels heading far out to sea and launching smaller boats to attack and hijack passing ships.

Somali pirates were at their peak during 2010 and 2011 – now thankfully it would appear that there is a downward trend for the first time in years. The combination of armed guards, military activity and pressure ashore have come together to make life harder for the pirate gangs, However, ships, including oil and chemical tankers, are still being attacked with automatic weapons and rocket-propelled grenade (RPG) launchers.

However, while there has been concentration on the Somali issue, there are a number of other regions in which piracy is real problem.

## Gulf of Guinea

Criminality, piracy and terrorism have long blighted Nigeria's waters and have slowly seeped further out into the wider Gulf of Guinea (GoG).

GoG is the large bight formed in the Atlantic Ocean, west of Africa. The countries bounding the GoG include Nigeria, Equatorial Guinea, Gabon, Liberia, Ghana, Togo, Cameroon, Benin and Ivory Coast.

Among the many rivers that drain into the GoG are the Niger and the Volta. The coastline on the gulf includes the Bight of Benin and the Bight of Bonny. The region is now regarded as one of the world's top oil and gas exploration hotspots.

The area has seen a long-running dispute between the Nigerian government and a group called the Movement for the Emancipation of the Niger Delta (MEND). This group has been responsible for a significant number of attacks on merchant shipping and oil and gas industry assets.

Despite occasional talks and mooted ceasefires the threat is real and continuing, meaning vessels need to be hardened for transits and operations in the area.

Recent years have seen piracy spread over the GoG and there are now numerous attacks off the coasts of many of the countries bounding the sea area.

While the primary drivers of Somali piracy are the value of the crew and vessel, the GoG brand of piracy tends to focus on stealing money or cargo, with the pirates much more likely to direct their violence towards the crew. There are many examples of violent attacks at sea that have resulted in death or serious injury to law-abiding seafarers simply going about their work. A standard type of attack will see a vessel hijacked and held while a (usually) liquid cargo is stolen. Once the cargo has been transferred onto another vessel the hijacked vessel is usually freed. However, there are concerns that pirates in the area are exploring the kidnap model, and this problem could be set to rise.

A surge in particularly violent and highly organised attacks has hit the coast of West Africa in recent years. According to the IMB's reports, the area is now the most significant piracy hotspot. There has been a surge in attacks on tankers off Benin, while vessels have also been hijacked and forced to sail to unknown locations where pirates ransacked and stole equipment and part of the product oil cargoes.

According to the IMB, the areas of concern include:

**Nigeria: Lagos and Bonny River –** Pirates are violent and have attacked and robbed vessels and kidnapped crews along the coast, rivers, anchorages, ports and surrounding waters. A number of crew members were injured in some of the attacks. Generally all Nigerian waters remain risky and vessels are also advised to be vigilant in other parts of Nigeria as many attacks may have gone unreported.

The PRC has received reports of boardings, vessels being fired upon and a number of attempted attacks. Crew have been beaten and threatened. Ship's equipment and crew's personal effects were stolen. According to the IMB, the seas around Nigeria are more dangerous than the official reports suggest. It is aware of a number of other incidents that were not reported to the PRC by Masters or owners.

**Guinea: Conakry –** Pirates armed with automatic weapons are violent and aggressive when attacking. In some attacks, pirates were dressed in military uniforms.

**Cameroon: Douala Outer Anchorage** – Two attacks with kidnapping of crews have occurred.

## South/Central America and the Caribbean

There has long been a problem with opportunistic attacks on vessels in various South and Central American ports and while anchored in the vicinity.

According to IMB reports:

**Brazil:** – Attacks have increased. Most attacks occurred at anchorage area

**Brazil: Santos** – Although the number of reported attacks has dropped, ships are advised to remain vigilant

**Peru: Callao** – Most attacks occurred at anchor despite vessels employing security watchmen

**Venezuela: Anchorages off Puerto La Cruz** – Intertanko has also released reports of piracy in the regions surrounding Barcelona City anchorages

**Haiti: Port-au-Prince** – Attacks have increased, especially in anchorage areas

**The Caribbean** often sees attacks on leisure craft and yachting

## Southeast Asia and the Indian Subcontinent

Long before the boom in piracy off Africa, attacks off Asian ports and inside the region's waters were commonplace. While various local and international initiatives have reduced the overall scale of attacks, the means and capability to attack ships still exist. It will perhaps come as no surprise when Asian piracy figures rise once again.

According to IMB reports:

**Bangladesh** – Still listed as high risk. Pirates are seen targeting ships preparing to anchor. Most attacks reported at Chittagong anchorages and approaches.

**Indonesia: Anambas, Natuna, Mangkai and Subi Besar islands area** – Pirates normally armed with guns, knives or machetes. Vigilance is needed in other areas. Many attacks may have gone unreported. Pirates normally attack at night. When spotted, pirates usually abort the attempted boarding.

**Malacca Strait –** Although the number of attacks has dropped due to the increased and aggressive patrols by the authorities of the littoral states since July 2005, ships are advised to continue maintaining a strict anti-piracy watch when transiting the strait. Currently, there are no indications as to how long these patrols will continue or when or if they will reduce.

**Malaysia off Tioman, Pulau Aur and the South China Sea –** Although no attacks reported recently, vessels are advised to remain vigilant. In the past, pirates armed with guns and knives have attacked vessels during the hours of darkness. A number of tugs and barges have been hijacked in the area.

**Singapore Strait –** Vessels are advised to continue maintaining adequate anti-piracy watch and measures despite the reduction in attacks. Pirates attack ships while under way or while anchored at the Eastern outer port limit areas.

**Vietnam –** Vung Tau often experiences opportunistic attacks.

## Types of piracy

The nature and scale of attacks in various locations changes frequently and CSOs, Masters and SSOs should be constantly aware of the up-to-date threats facing them.

Two basic types of piracy have developed: crimes of opportunity where vessels are boarded and the pirates make off with whatever isn't bolted down (seaborne muggers); more sinister, violent, planned raids in which pirates seem to be party to information concerning ships, their routes and cargoes.

Organised crime continues to be an increasing part of the piracy problem. According to the IMO, a number of Asian crime syndicates with mafia-style organisations in Indonesia, the Philippines, Hong Kong and mainland China have enough trans-national sophistication to make money from high seas piracy on a regular basis.

The two types of piracy can be distinguished into four different methods of attack:

### Opportunistic crime (OC)

By far the most common form of piracy as it requires no planning. If a target appears at the wrong place and the wrong time there is a risk of this type of attack. Weapons may play a part in such a raid but on the whole the ship is simply robbed without recourse to violence. Many vessels do not even know that such attacks have occurred until it becomes apparent that things have gone missing (mooring ropes are a favourite). These small thefts often occur within ports or port waters and complicate the wider issue of piracy.

### Low-level armed robbery (LLAR)

Perpetrators use high-speed craft (usually launched from a land base) and an assortment of weaponry to board a vessel. The view held is that the people who carry out such raids are often petty criminals who view ships as soft targets. For this reason it would be safe to assume that as long as the ship's personnel do not act rashly they will not be in too much danger.

### Medium-level armed assault and robbery (MLAAR)

This type of attack is often meticulously planned. Experienced seafarers and a mixture of criminal elements are often involved. They come together to form formidable pirate gangs. MLAAR attacks often use a trawler or some other larger vessel as a mother ship from which to launch the attack using small high-speed craft. The pirates in these cases are heavily armed and these attacks often bear the hallmarks of professional military involvement. There is a very high risk of injury or death for innocent seafarers involved, although with a certain degree of luck and good management it may be possible to comply with the pirates' demands without putting too many of the ship's personnel at risk. This type of highly precise raid is characteristic of many areas around southeast Asia and has become increasingly popular off Somalia.

### Major criminal hijack (MCHJ)

This used to be the domain of the underworld and organised criminals as they stole cargoes and created 'phantom' ships. Since the outbreak of hijack for ransom off Somalia, MCHJ now takes two forms.

The first is a very professional hit that requires information, pinpoint accuracy and substantial resources. A vessel experiencing such an attack will be boarded by a large number of highly organised and heavily-armed criminals. There are two different outcomes to such a raid. In the first, the vessel may be held by the pirates until another vessel can rendezvous and the ship's cargo is transferred; or the cargo will be kept onboard the ship, which will be given a new identity and very often a new paint scheme.

In many MCHJ attacks the genuine ship's crew are disposed of in a violent manner and replaced by the hijacker's own personnel.

# Methods of attack

Until the attacks began off Somalia, most pirate attacks were made at night. Somali pirates are, however, more brazen and will attack in daylight with guns blazing. They will also on occasion attack on bright moonlit nights. Despite this change, it is helpful to look at attacks under two headings:

- Attacks alongside or at anchor
- Attacks while under way

In both cases, pirates may climb up mooring ropes and anchor chains or scale the ship's side from small boats. They have also been known to enter ships via gangways, bunker and stores and pilot access points.

# Precautions alongside or at anchor

- Strict control must be maintained at all gangways and accesses, allowing only those who are identified and authorised on board
- Large effective rat-guards must be placed on mooring ropes, out of reach of the ship's side and the jetty
- Fairleads and hawse pipes should be sealed, allowing no human access
- At night, all upper deck lighting should be on at full brilliance and extra lighting should be rigged as necessary over the ship's stern and seaward side as necessary to eliminate dark areas. Powerful search or arc lights are preferable
- All upper deck lockers should be locked, also any accesses leading to accommodation or technical areas that are not strictly needed for the period during which the ship is alongside or at anchor
- Upper deck patrols should be maintained at all times during the hours of darkness
- In dangerous areas, tendering of passengers after dark should be avoided and accommodation ladders should be raised

## Attacks when under way

The method of attacking vessels while under way has altered as a result of activity by Somali pirates. However, small boats are generally used with a group of pirates (usually six or eight) on board to approach the target vessel's side or stern.

They then enter into a 'stalking' phase in which they assess their prey vessel. If the risk is deemed acceptable and they see little in the way of personnel activity, they will approach the ship. They wish to force the crew to panic and make the vessel stop, so will often lay down a cover of fire from assault rifles and RPGs at the target vessel.

Precautions when under way will be addressed later in the handbook as part of the overview of Best Management Practices as laid down for commercial shipping operating in or near areas of pirate threat (see page 23).

# Chapter 3
## Practical measures to tackle piracy

### KEY ADVICE

- Understanding pirate actions
- Understanding how to implement Best Management Practices
- Assessing risk management techniques
- Planning transits
- Understanding reporting procedures

For Somali pirates the goal is to place their skiffs alongside the ship being attacked to enable one or more armed pirates to climb onboard. Pirates frequently use long, lightweight ladders and ropes, or a long hooked pole with a knotted climbing rope, to climb up the side of the vessel being attacked.

Once onboard, the pirate(s) will generally make their way to the bridge to take control of the vessel. Once on the bridge, they will demand that the ship slows or stops to enable further pirates to board.

Four basic tactics will minimise the risk posed by pirates:

- Avoid
- Evade
- Deter
- Delay

Perhaps the most useful form of risk mitigation is simply to avoid pirates by ensuring the vessel never comes across them in the first place.

Some say this is based on luck but with the increasing levels of good intelligence available, it seems that knowing your enemy and how to avoid them can be a key factor. When vessels have to head into high risk areas, they need to ensure their Masters are aware of the threats and of the best routes to minimise the risk of being targeted.

# Essential considerations in the High Risk Area

## Freeboard

- It is likely that pirates will try to board the ship being attacked at the lowest point above the waterline, making it easier for them to climb onboard. These points are often on either quarter or at the vessel's stern
- Experience suggests that vessels with a minimum freeboard greater than 8m have a much greater chance of successfully escaping a piracy attempt than those with less
- A large freeboard will provide little or no protection if the construction of the ship provides access assistance to pirates seeking to climb onboard. In this case, further protective measures should be considered
- A large freeboard alone may not be enough to deter a pirate attack

## Speed

- One of the most effective ways to defeat a pirate attack is by using speed to try to outrun the attackers or make it difficult to board
- To date, there have been no reported attacks where pirates have boarded a ship that has been proceeding at over 18kt. It is possible, however, that pirate tactics and techniques may develop to enable them to board faster-moving ships.
- Ships are recommended to proceed at full sea speed in the high risk area (HRA), or at least 18kt where they are capable of greater speed, throughout their transit of the HRA

If ships cannot avoid the high risk areas, it is important to be able to keep one step ahead. The secret to evading pirates rests on the ability to spot attackers at sufficient distance to be able to react. Effective watchkeeping is vitally important.

If a vessel is capable of sufficient speed, it can be as simple as full ahead and pulling away from danger. For slower vessels, the problems are a little more complex.

Many Masters have honed their ship-handling skills over years but the techniques they learn are all about minimising contact or damage to other vessels, or making it easier for others coming alongside. When faced with pirates, they have to think differently and apply opposite, new techniques to try to get the ship away from the pirates. It can be challenging using a ship defensively, but can be very effective.

If it becomes apparent that evading the attack has failed, it is imperative that some form of defensive measures is put in place on and around the vessel to deter attackers attempting to board.

These can come in many forms, ranging from passive to proactive. Common passive tools include razor wire.

The current popularity of armed defence has stemmed from deterring attackers. An increasing number of reports state that pirates have been forced to turn away from vessels when security teams have returned fire. At the moment the armed response is seemingly the most effective deterrent.

If the worst happens and pirates board the vessel, all is not quite lost. The next phase relies on the crew being able to delay the pirates, while hoping for a rapid response from naval assets.

The citadel approach has become popular and, when implemented properly, it can buy time for a military response. However, the citadel defence is not without its own hazards.

## Best Management Practices

Given the threat facing many vessels, it is clear that much work has to be done to ensure that crews and their ships have some form of self-protection regime in place. One element of this is the SSP prepared under the requirements of the ISPS Code. This becomes a vital tool in deterring pirates, reacting to them and responding to the consequences of their attacks.

The SSP exists to solve all security issues, allowing those onboard to access the information and details of their required security responses. While the plan covers much more than piracy, it is important that its contents provide personnel with the means to tackle not just the 'soft' side of security, such as administration, but also the 'hard' side.

The BMP, continuously reviewed and updated (version current at time of going to press BMP4 *Best Management Practices for Protection against Somalia Based Piracy*), assist companies and seagoing personnel to avoid, evade, deter or delay attacks by Somali pirates. Fundamental requirements are:

**Report to UKMTO** – This is the primary point of contact for merchant vessels and liaison with military forces in the region and the primary point of contact during an attack. UKMTO should be aware of vessels transiting the HRA

**Register at MSCHOA** – In addition to the usual bounding areas, the Strait of Hormuz is now included

**Implement self-protection measures**

# Basic advice on how to avoid being a victim of piracy

- Do not be alone
- Report. Use the international recommended transit corridor (IRTC). Keep AIS on
- Do not be detected
- Use navigation lights only at night. Follow NAV WARNINGS
- Do not be surprised. Be vigilant
- Do not be vulnerable. Implement self-protection measures
- Do not be boarded. Use speed and manoeuvres
- Do not be controlled. Carry out drills. Citadel provision. Control access

Experience, supported by data collected by naval forces, shows that the application of such recommendations can make a significant difference in preventing a ship becoming a victim of piracy. The number of vessels which have been able to deter pirates attacking, or which have been able to prevent them boarding, has been on the rise of late. Many vessels which have used armed guards or razor wire and water cannon have been able to avoid hijack by implementing appropriate measures to protect themselves.

The HRA for piracy attacks defines itself by where pirate activity and attacks have taken place.

There are four entry to exit boundaries to and from the HRA: 78°E, 23°N, 10°S, Suez and Port (local). Attacks have taken place at all extremities of the HRA. Attacks to the south have extended into the Mozambique Channel. A high state of readiness and vigilance should be maintained even to the south of the southerly limit of the HRA.

The HRA does change and pirates can strike outside this zone. Vigilance is necessary across an ever expanding sea area. Masters and companies should have access to the latest attack data and information on the risks and threats facing them on any particular voyage.

If in doubt, a vessel should act as if in the HRA and BMP guidance should be followed in full. The range of procedures offers sensible and relatively simple ways to better safeguard against attack.

# Risk assessment

This is an important aspect of maritime security. Slower and lower vessels are at greater risk than those with a high freeboard and travelling at a higher speed.

According to BMP, the factors to be considered in the risk assessment cover:

- Crew safety – Assessing access control versus safety, especially in the event of shipboard emergencies
- Location of a safe muster point or citadel
- Ballistic protection for crew on the bridge
- Freeboard – As stated previously, pirates usually try to board at the lowest point above the waterline. Usually vessels with a freeboard greater than 8m are less likely to be boarded. However, freeboard may provide little or no protection if other access points are provided
- Speed – To date, there have been no reported attacks where pirates have boarded a ship that has been proceeding at over 18kt. It is possible, however, that pirate tactics and techniques may develop to enable them to board faster-moving ships
- Sea state – Pirates attack from small craft (skiffs) which are often more difficult to operate if the sea state is 3 or above

The risk assessment must be ship and voyage specific, not generic. While the freeboard and speed of passage can make a vessel safer, it is important to perform a full risk assessment to formally gauge vulnerabilities. Issues such as crew size, weather conditions and proximity to other attacks also play a part in this assessment.

The BMP stress the tactics used by pirates. Pirates attack vessels in skiffs (small boats with powerful outboard motors), often carrying six pirates or more. Attacks may involve multiple skiffs approaching from different directions.

Once within range, the pirates begin to lay down volleys of suppressing fire from automatic weapons or RPGs in an attempt to board and hijack vessels. This fire is intended to scare and intimidate the crew into slowing down or allowing them the freedom to board.

While the fire from such weapons can be terrifying it seldom creates much damage to the vessel. Ships are surprisingly robust in the face of such firepower. However, reports are emerging of some pirate gangs using more sophisticated and heavier weaponry, such as the RPG-29, and there are even rumours of man-portable air defence systems. These are basically shoulder-launched surface-to-air missiles.

If the attack is successful and the vessel hijacked, the pirates usually sail towards the Somali coast and thereafter demand a ransom for the release of the vessel and crew.

# Implementing BMP

There is no 'one size fits all' solution. Every vessel has to be assessed properly and where the lessons of others can be learned and applied this should be done.

As with all aspects of maritime security, management of piracy and hijack protection requires collaboration between management ashore and those onboard. Workable and pragmatic solutions are based on a combined and unified effort.

BMP stress the importance of reporting from ashore and the management and accessing of information. A well briefed CSO can make all the difference, but one who is able to engage with law enforcement and the military is even better.

Some companies may wish to revisit their assessment of what constitutes safe manning and may decide that additional personnel are needed for particular voyages. Everyone onboard should be confident and knowledgeable about their role and the duties they are to undertake.

The responsibilities of the CSO and the SSO are laid down in the ISPS Code. Essential reading is the MSC circular giving guidance to CSOs on preparation of a company and crew for the contingency of hijack by pirates in the Western Indian Ocean and the Gulf of Aden (MSC.1/Circ.1390). This supplements existing guidelines and should be used in conjunction with existing security provisions.

# BMP reporting procedures

An essential part of BMP that applies to all ships is liaison with naval forces. The two key naval organisations to contact are the UK Maritime Trade Operations (UKMTO) and the Maritime Security Centre Horn of Africa (MSCHOA).

UKMTO's reporting process incorporates initial report, daily reports and final report (upon departure or port arrival).

It is important that vessels and their operators complete both the UKMTO Vessel Position Reporting Forms and register with MSCHOA, which has significantly expanded the area in which vessels must register to bring this in line with UKMTO requirements.

Compliance enables MSCHOA to have a full profile of the vessel, its dimensions and all security measures in order that a vulnerability risk assessment can be made. This information is used by MSCHOA watchkeepers to inform naval assets at sea. Vessels need to register to MSCHOA only once each entry.

It also enables full risk analysis of vessel registrations to be carried out by flag, owner, ship type, cargo, self-protection measures and any contracted security. This important data allows militaries to work with flag states, industry organisations and ship operators to analyse pirate trends and prepare updated advice. This ultimately enables more informed BMP updates, preparation of SSPs and demonstrates the shipping industry's efforts to fight piracy.

Many vessels are not registering the presence of private armed security with MSCHOA. This information is important to enable full operational understanding of the threats and vulnerability in the HRA. Information concerning the presence of armed security onboard vessels will not be passed to flag states or industry organisations.

If vessel registration is not made under these conditions, the ship is NOT BMP-compliant as recognised by the shipping Industry including the IMO, the military and flag states.

# Planning prior to transit

BMP stress the importance of the role of Master and the steps that should be taken to plan for the passage through these dangerous waters and of the need to ensure that vessel movements are communicated to the correct channels.

The Master should know what response is expected in this regard when entering or near the HRA.

Emphasis should also be placed on briefing of crew and conducting drills. Consideration should also be given to testing of self-protection measures and the security of all access points and a thorough review of the SSP.

A key part of the pre-transit planning is the ship's AIS policy. The current recommendation is to keep AIS on. However, a number of organisations have questioned this and there could be further changes as industry does not feel that a generic stance is helpful. The issue of AIS usage in the HRA has been the subject of conjecture and debate – it is felt by many that the Master is in the best position to assess whether to keep the AIS on, and it would perhaps be advisable for the CSO and Master to enter into dialogue about this difficult and potentially contentious issue.

The Master should ensure that BMP measures are in place prior to entry into the HRA. While any maintenance and engineering work should be kept to a minimum in the HRA, BMP contain guidance and clear controls if work has to be performed.

Masters are advised to have an enhanced policy for daily vessel reporting to UKMTO via email and this should be completed daily at 0800 GMT. Masters are encouraged to carefully review all warnings and information and should be willing and able to make voyage routeing changes if necessary.

Masters are advised to prepare an emergency communication plan that will include all emergency contact numbers and prepared messages.

# International Recommended Transit Corridor

In 2009, MSCHOA established the International Recommended Transit Corridor (IRTC), in which military assets (naval and air) are strategically deployed to best provide protection and support to merchant ships.

Masters using the IRTC are not relieved of their obligation and should continue to maintain a strict 24-hour lookout using all available means to get an early warning of an approaching threat. Some vessels have been attacked or hijacked in the corridor.

Vessels are advised that these are not convoys and they should not wait for warships or other merchant vessels but proceed at the recommended times.

Vessels of different speeds will converge in critical areas at the critical times. Vessels may be contacted by warships in the vicinity if they have registered their transit details on the MSCHOA website.

The IRTC is not a traffic separation scheme, nor is it marked with navigational aids and vessels are to comply with the requirements of the International Regulations for Preventing Collisions at Sea at all times. The premise behind the IRTC and the Group Transit (GT) is that it allows naval forces to ensure that the areas of highest risk within the Gulf of Aden are sanitised at the times of greatest risk (around sunrise and sunset) and that groups of vessels are together in these locations at these times.

It is strongly recommended that ships navigate within the IRTC where naval forces are concentrated and operate the GT scheme, coordinated by MSCHOA. This scheme groups vessels together by speed for maximum protection for their transit through the IRTC.

Use of the GT scheme is recommended. Masters should note that warships might not be within visual range of the ships in the GT, but this does not lessen the protection afforded by the scheme.

Some countries offer independent convoy escorts through the IRTC where merchant vessels are escorted by a warship. Details of the convoy schedules and how to apply to be included in an escort are detailed on the MSCHOA website (www.mschoa.org). It should be noted that most national convoys require prior registration to enable vessels to join. The same points as noted above apply when timing arrival at the forming-up point for a convoy.

The IRTC runs in a NE (072°)-SW (252°) orientation and the usual rendezvous points for joining are:

- Point A: 11-50N, 045-00E
- Point B: 14-28N, 053-00E

Masters are advised to make adjustments to passage plans to conform to MSCHOA general and routeing advice. It should also be noted that "group transits" are not "convoys". Ships joining a GT should:

- Carefully time their arrival to avoid a slow speed approach to the forming-up point (A or B)
- Avoid waiting at the forming-up point (A or B)
- Note that ships are particularly vulnerable to a pirate attack if they slowly approach or wait at the forming up points (A and B)

# Post-incident reporting

Post-incident reporting will enable better allocation of naval and law enforcement assets and will assist in any impending prosecution of pirates or financiers.

BMP encourage owners to provide a copy of any post-incident reports to the IMB. It is also stressed that any report should contain descriptions and distinguishing features of any suspicious vessels that were observed.

Law enforcement authorities will routinely request permission to conduct post-release crew debriefs and to collect evidence for future investigations and prosecutions following captivity. A thorough investigation is critical to ensure that potential physical evidence, including electronic, is not tainted or destroyed or potential witnesses overlooked. The company and crew are advised that the quality of the evidence provided and the availability of the crew to testify will significantly help any investigation or prosecution that follows.

INTERPOL has a secure website to provide support to ship operators who have had their vessels hijacked by pirates. Its Maritime Piracy Task Force can assist in taking the appropriate steps to preserve the integrity of the evidence left behind at the crime scene. INTERPOL has a Command and Co-ordination Centre (CCC) that supports any of the 188 member countries faced with a crisis or requiring urgent operational assistance. The CCC operates in English, French, Spanish and Arabic and is staffed 24 hours a day, 365 days a year. It is recommended ship operators contact INTERPOL within three days of a hijacking.

INTERPOL may be consulted to discuss the recommended best practices and protocols for the preservation of evidence or other physical clues that could be useful to law enforcement agents pursuing an investigation of the incident. Contact details are contained in the latest edition of BMP.

# West Africa Interim Guidelines

In response to the recent increase in the level of attacks against shipping, industry organisations (including Bimco, ICS, Intercargo and Intertanko) have issued Interim Guidelines for Owners, Operators and Masters for protection against piracy in the Gulf of Guinea region.

Although piracy in the GoG region differs in many ways from that off Somalia, the guidelines make the point that large sections of the BMP, developed to protect against piracy off Somalia, will also be valid in the GoG region. The

Interim Guidelines should therefore be read in conjunction with the advice contained in the latest BMP.

The position in the GoG is continuing to evolve and it is anticipated that the Interim Guidelines, which aim to bridge the gap between the advice currently found in BMP4 and the prevailing situation in the GoG region, will be subject to updating and revision, as and when required.

Their focus is therefore to use the BMPs to counter what is similar while equipping the shipping industry with a means of appreciating and dealing with the key differences. For example, generally speaking pirates in the GoG are more violent and their 'pirate business model' does not primarily involve kidnap for ransom (although there are concerns this is on the rise). Generally, the crew of a ship does not in itself represent the 'value', whereas the cargo does.

Image: USCG

# Chapter 4
## Tools to tackle piracy

### KEY ADVICE

- Understanding the use and importance of good intelligence
- Assessing the range of anti-piracy equipment
- Understanding how to manage security guards
- Making decisions on the use of armed guards
- Assessing future trends and developments

Responding to the threat of piracy demands a joined-up approach that involves the company, CSO, SSO, Master and shipboard personnel. It is also important to remember the role of various international organisations and the military.

Key to success is the provision of intelligence, which allows those in pirate hotspots to increase their vigilance and remain aware of the threat and the means of evading, avoiding, deterring or delaying it.

While the BMP have had a very positive effect on the ships that implement them, there is sadly an underclass of sub-standard shipping. Crews on such vessels are not made aware of the threats, do not receive information on where they may be in danger or of the simple measures they can take to keep themselves safe. Intelligence, data and information are vital keys in safeguarding ships and lessons need to be learned from the mistakes of others.

It is vital that all are aware of the genuine threats to the vessel and when they are at their peak. Onboard resources are finite and the shipboard response must be adapted in reaction to the reality – neither too relaxed and unprepared or starting at shadows.

Key to this is an appreciation of both the *modus operandi* of the pirates and their operational parameters. Knowing about the cyclical nature of attacks and the seasonal monsoon weather patterns and the effects these have on the fleets of small Somali boats is important. So too is up-to-date information, as without real-time, detailed knowledge it is easy to expend vital resources or become complacent.

The threat of piracy evolves constantly and rapidly, and so it is vitally important to stay on top of the most recent reports, trends and data. There are numerous sources of information and intelligence available – including non-commercial sources such as:

The International Maritime Bureau (IMB) www.icc-ccs.org
The NATO Shipping Centre (NSC) www.shipping.nato.int
The US Office of Naval Intelligence www.oni.navy.mil
The Security Association for the Maritime Industry www.seasecurity.org

Most P&I clubs also provide excellent resources and there are also a range of commercial alternatives providing data and intelligence.

# Anti-piracy equipment

A huge and constantly evolving industry supplies equipment ranging from barbed wire to Kevlar vests and anti-pirate lasers. However, these lists contain various pieces of equipment which sound wonderful in theory and look amazing in the brochures, but which do not deliver in the face of a pirate onslaught.

CSOs are advised to work closely with trusted providers and to research thoroughly before investing in equipment that turns out to be unsuited to their vessels or crews or not actually fit for purpose.

The advice is always to buy the best quality basics, such as razor wire, while remaining suitably dubious about the claims of more high-tech equipment until it is possible to either test or trial it.

More details on security equipment can be found in The Nautical Institute publication (Steven Jones, *Maritime Security: a practical guide*, second edition published 2012).

# Ship protection measures

BMP advice rests on the premise that "if pirates are unable to board a ship, they cannot hijack it".

Vessels are advised to consider a shorter rotation of the watch period in order to maximise alertness of the lookouts. Use of anti-glare binoculars is encouraged.

A key foundation of ship protection measures is being able to identify potential attackers early and at distance. "A proper lookout is the single most effective method of ship protection, where early warning of a suspicious approach or attack is assured, and where defences can be readily deployed."

Flying glass is a major issue when the bridge is attacked and the use of security glass film (often called blast-resistant film) is encouraged.

In order to protect from RPG-7 shells, the guidance states that "the sides and rear of the bridge and the bridge wings may be protected with a double layer of chain link fence, which has been shown to reduce the effect of an RPG round. Proprietary anti-RPG screens are also available."

In assessing the importance of access control and of deterring or delaying access to pirates, the guidance stresses that if pirates do gain access to the upper deck of a vessel they will be tenacious in their efforts to gain access to the accommodation section and the bridge in particular. It is strongly recommended that significant effort is expended prior to entry to the HRA to deny the pirates access to the accommodation and the bridge, should they overcome the vessel's self-protective measures and board the vessel.

All doors and hatches providing access should be properly secured. Additional securing, such as with wire strops, is advised for hatches where possible.

BMP guidance stresses that pirates have been known to gain access through portholes and windows. Fitting steel bars to windows will prevent this even if they manage to shatter the window.

It is vital to have accommodation lock-down procedures. BMP advice is that prior to entering the HRA, such procedures should be detailed in a set of Master's standing orders including a checklist to ensure all applicable openings to the accommodation, machinery spaces and store rooms are safely secured.

Physical barriers have been discussed in earlier incarnations of BMP. In the latest guidance it is advised that such barriers "should be used to make it as difficult as possible to gain access to vessels by increasing the height and difficulty of any climb for an attacking pirate."

# BMP guidance on physical barriers

- Razor wire is still offered as an extremely effective barrier. The advice is to combine this with chain link fence. Any razor wire should be secured so pirates cannot pull it off with, for instance, the hook of their boarding ladder. Consideration should also be given to securing the razor wire with a wire strop to prevent it being dislodged
- Gaps in the razor wire will be exploited
- Anti-climb paint is no longer considered an effective measure
- If electric fences are to be used, then a full risk assessment is to be carried out
- Water cannons are a useful ship protection measure. However, in order to use all ship's pumps extra power may be required. This is may require classification society input
- Steam is cited as an effective deterrent, as are 'water spray rails'.
- Use of foam is covered and it is stressed that any supplies used must be in addition to the ships fire-fighting equipment stock

Where possible no maintenance should be carried out on the vessel's sea water systems while on passage in the HRA.

In order to utilise all pumps, additional power may be required and therefore these systems should also be ready for immediate use.

Practice, observation and drills will be required in order to ensure that the results achieved by the equipment provide effective coverage of vulnerable areas.

Use of alarms and sound signals is covered. If approached, continuous sounding of the vessel's foghorn or whistle distracts the pirates. It also lets them know they have been seen.

New emphasis is placed on manoeuvring practice. Practising prior to entry into the HRA will be very beneficial and ensure familiarity with the ship's handling characteristics and how to effect anti-piracy manoeuvres while maintaining the best possible speed.

It is stressed that waiting until the ship is attacked before practising is too late!

# Private security – armed or unarmed

As the threat from pirates has increased, the response of many shipping companies has been to look to private security providers for assistance and guidance. Initially this often took the form of training and guidance on the application of security onboard. However, as the incidents of piracy continued unabated, an increasing number of shipowners turned to armed guards as a form of protection and deterrent.

Hiring of professional, armed security personnel has increasingly been seen as an effective way of protecting ships. However, it should be stressed that the use of armed guards should only follow a full risk assessment, and be used as a response to the vulnerabilities identified.

There is a section within BMP dedicated to the use of private maritime security contractors (PMSC), whether armed or unarmed. The guidance states: "use of unarmed private maritime security contractors is a matter for individual ship operators following their own voyage risk assessment. The deployment onboard [is] subject to the national laws of the flag state. The use of experienced and competent unarmed private maritime security contractors can be a valuable addition to BMP."

The shipping industry has recognised that an increasing number of owners and operators wish to deploy armed guards on board their vessels but has made it clear that deployment of armed guards is a matter for each individual owner:

● IMO: "a decision for the individual shipowner after a thorough risk assessment and after ensuring all other practical means of self protection have been employed"
● BMP: "a matter for individual shipowners to decide following their own voyage risk assessment and approval of respective Flag States"
● BMP does not contain a specific endorsement of their use: "this advice does not constitute a recommendation or an endorsement of the general use of armed private maritime security contractors"

It is clear, therefore, that use of armed PMSCs must be approved by the flag state and seen as an additional layer of protection and not an alternative to BMP.

If armed PMSCs are present on board a merchant vessel, this fact should be included in reports to UKMTO and MSCHOA.

The IMO has produced guidance for shipowners, ship operators and Shipmasters on the use of privately contracted armed security personnel on board ships in the high risk area. Full details of these guidelines can be found in The Nautical Institute publication *Maritime Security: a practical guide*, second edition, 2012.

There have also been concerns over the legitimacy and legality of weapons used by some armed teams. A number of P&I clubs have warned members with vessels that may have guns or ammunition on board and are trading to certain countries. The clubs have stated that all should be aware of local regulations relating to all vessels carrying weapons or ammunition. Failure to comply can result in the arrest of the Master.

# Management of security teams

The increasing use of security teams onboard has created an interesting and challenging dilemma for senior shipboard officers, particularly the Master.

Hopefully for those onboard, the security team has been employed from a company of repute and not only are the team's skills and equipment up to the task but they will be well trained and aware of the management structure onboard the vessel. It is also to be hoped that they have experience of previous shipboard operations.

The CSO and the maritime security provider should be in dialogue to ensure that any personnel supplied are able to operate within the challenging shipboard environment, and that sufficient vetting of company and personnel has taken place.

It is important for the CSO to communicate with the Master to ensure awareness of who is coming onboard, the scope of their employment and the equipment they will be bringing. It is also important that the Master is made fully aware of their rules of engagement and standard operating procedures if they are armed.

Once onboard, the Master and security team leader should have a meeting to further set out the scope of their responsibilities, watch patterns and any particular requirements each party will have. The security personnel should be taken through the normal SMS requirements for new joiners, such as familiarisation, muster stations and alarms.

It would also be desirable to gather as many of the shipboard personnel together to formally meet and be introduced to the security team. In an ideal situation, the partnership and strength of the bond between crew and the riding team can boost the effectiveness of the security response.

There is currently no 'one size fits all' solution to the management of security teams and this area will no doubt evolve as the taking on of such support becomes the norm. Each company and each Master should look to develop detailed feedback and their own internal best practice to ensure they are able to secure the vessel effectively and get the very best from the teams placed onboard.

Despite the standards imposed by the IMO on security providers, not every security team member will have a maritime background and many teams may not have worked together on previous assignments. This means there is a great deal to organise prior to the transit of hostile waters.

The team leader should engage fully and openly with the Master and should be appreciative of the line of command and respectful of the decisions made by shipboard personnel. There may also be cultural aspects to be addressed and the security team should be sensitive to these.

It is vital that the security team settle in to their new surroundings and get to know the vessel and the personnel onboard. While there is much for the security team to teach, there is also much to learn.

Prior to embarking on such employment it is strongly recommended that security personnel who do not have a naval or maritime background should have a minimum grounding and education in the practical realities of the ship (eg navigation, control and handling) and on the implications of their role onboard.

Anecdotally there are increasing reports of security personnel, even senior people, referring to charts as "maps" and chart positions as "coordinates". While these lapses are not perhaps overly serious in themselves, they do serve to potentially undermine the perception of the experience and skill of the security team. The best and most effective security teams work within an atmosphere of trust, respect and mutual understanding, and all efforts should be expended to make this a reality.

# Setting the standards

The issue of privately contracted armed security personnel (PCASP) onboard ships has long been a sensitive and contested topic. While the IMO has issued guidance on the matter, ultimately it has been agreed that the International

Organization for Standardization (ISO) would be best placed to develop international standards.

In response to this, ISO developed a standard for the assessment of PMSCs, which provides reassurance that the maritime security industry is responsible, professional and effective, while also:

- Improving accountability
- Helping clients to identify competent companies
- Raising standards internationally

This is not a stand-alone standard as it plugs into ISO 28000, a supply chain security standard already in government-recognised use with critical supply chains.

This high level management standard enables an organisation to establish an overall risk-based approach to managing any disruptive event in the supply chain – before, during and after the event. Piracy was deemed as fitting into this remit.

ISO/PAS 28007:2012 has been developed to provide guidelines containing additional sector-specific recommendations. Utilising the existing knowledge of the ISO 28000 framework, the maritime security standard takes advantage of the potential for:

- Certification
- Accreditation
- Legal compliance regimes

It sets the gold standard for PMSCs which want to demonstrate to the international community that they and the operatives they supply are of the right quality to legally, safely and effectively guard commercial shipping on the high seas.

Compliance with ISO/PAS 28007:2012 will ultimately classify a PMSC as providing PCASP. The key components include: management of the security system (security risk assessments, key management responsibilities clearly defined, legal and other regulatory requirements and internal audits of operations); procedural aspects (rules of authority, contractor selection, screening and vetting, authorising licensing of firearms, prevention of incidents, incident management and emergency response, investigation and reporting of incidents, procedures for detainment, identification, interface with crew and familiarisation).

# Contractual agreements

As the use of private security increases, the Baltic and International Maritime Council (BIMCO) has produced a standardised contract between shipowners and private maritime security companies called Guardcon. This provides clarity on a range of key issues and does cover the relationship between the Master and the security team leader (TL) on board.

Guardcon has emerged as the standard contract for the employment of security guards on vessels. It was developed to provide shipowners and PMSCs with a clearly worded and comprehensive standard contract to govern the employment and use of security guards, with or without firearms, on board merchant vessels.

# Rules for the Use of Force

When the military engage with an enemy, they do so under what are termed Rules of Engagement. For the private security industry, armed guards are governed by the civilian equivalent, Rules for the Use of Force (RUF).

One major issue facing the shipping industry as it has turned to using armed guards was the absence of a standard, accepted and legally tested set of RUF. This has been a serious concern.

Eventually key maritime industry stakeholders, flag states, maritime insurers and the private maritime security industry worked together to consider standardised RUF when armed guards employed on commercial vessels are forced to respond to pirate attacks.

This saw the production of the 100 Series Rules for the Use of Force. The aim of these simplified numbered rules is to provide a logical and easily managed escalation and de-escalation of deterrence to complement BIMCO's Guardcon and ISO/PAS 28007:2012 as the international RUF benchmark standard.

PCASP are trained to respond to threats facing vessels in a "reasonable, necessary and proportionate" manner.

The 100 Series rules are seen as a vital pillar in the provision of maritime security.

They represent the first international model set of RUF for the benefit of, and use by, the entire maritime industry. While they will not provide any form of indemnity or immunity against civil or criminal liability when force has been used unlawfully, there is now a model against which PCASP may be professionally trained; companies audited and operator actions measured and judged by competent authorities.

The rules have undergone stringent operator, commercial and legal scrutiny from across the maritime industry, and at the core is the basic principle of the individual right of self-defence; itself a universal concept and which can now be tied into a formal audit trail to prove the proper steps have been applied in protecting life at sea.

If used and applied correctly, the rules ensure the response will be constant and consistent. If lives are threatened, then the RUF will be invoked and a graduated response will provide adequate time for pirates to break off their attack, or face a heightened reaction.

## The Master's authority: safety versus security

Outside any specific contractual implications, it is correct to say that the Master retains overall control but there are concerns that this control can be called into question if there are armed guards onboard.

The legal implications and potential liability have naturally been a concern and have been discussed within the IMO. There are natural concerns where the actions of PCASP may cause injury or death to any person, including the PCASP themselves, or other damage to the ship or its cargo.

Understandably, different opinions were voiced as to what extent the Master could be held liable in such cases. There was concern over the possible legal consequences a ship's Master could face. As Masters are deemed to have "overriding authority", this could be construed in such a way that they could be held ultimately responsible for any actions taken by the PCASP which were actually beyond the Master's control.

Masters are increasingly concerned about this. Guidelines explaining amendments from the Norwegian Maritime Directorate reflect this issue and take a view from the command and control structure perspective. They are contained in the Directorate's Ship Security Regulation of 22 June 2004 No 972 (security measures on board ships and mobile offshore drilling units) that came into force in July 2011. They also recognise the importance in contract documentation of a clear statement that at all times the Master remains in command and retains the overriding authority on board. The distinction between the use of the terms "authority" and "responsibility" was noted – something it is hoped will protect all parties when there is any future apportionment of liability.

It is perhaps important here to better define and address what is meant by the terms "responsibility and "authority".

- Responsibility is often seen to imply a relationship and a person being "responsible" to ensure something happens in the expected manner. This of course has implications as the Master may be responsible through the relationship with the armed team to ensure the safety of those involved and that the correct RUF are imposed and adhered to. Such a wide ranging and heavy burden may well be difficult for the Master to carry
- Authority, conversely, relates to a function or title, as the person authorised to make decisions

It has yet to be tested in law, but it would seem that the Master has the authority, but should not be burdened with an unacceptable and unreasonable level of responsibility.

There has long been concern over the basic interactions between Master and crew and PCASPs. Some operatives strike up wonderfully positive working relationships with those onboard, while others do not. It is important, therefore, that the Master and crew should be briefed on the HRA, location and duration of the ship's passage, the role of the PCASP within the security plan and watch schedule and the crew's actions when under attack. This is about understanding the threat posed, actions taken to minimise the risk and actions all can expect to witness and be relied upon to perform.

Until something goes wrong and a court case ensues, the full legal ramifications of the issue of shipboard command and control can only be guessed at. However, written by leading lawyers and with wide support from the shipping industry, it seems the 100 Series RUF will do much to alleviate some of the key concerns as they enshrine the concept of self-defence and also mitigate the "joint enterprise" fears that Masters could be implicated for the actions of guards.

# Trends and developments

Different categories of piracy, as discussed previously, carry with them differing tactics and focus. The most prevalent form of piracy today is that which has developed off Somalia, but as progress is made in the Indian Ocean then the latest piracy epidemic looks set to take hold off West Africa.

The problems of piracy have highlighted the "move and counter-move" basis on which piracy is battled or countered. Ships implement protective measures only to see pirates then trying to overcome them. This escalates over time until, hopefully, piracy in the particular area or region is nullified.

Whether off Somalia or in the Gulf of Guinea, there is every indication that piracy problems are set to get worse in the coming years. Each region has its own trends and developments, and peaks and troughs of activity, and these have serious implications onboard ship.

# Somali-based piracy

Despite a lull in activities, and seeming containment of the problem, pirate groups are still determined and desperate. It will take solutions ashore to fully contain the problem. Despite successes, with the financial incentives so great, it seems there remains a danger of an escalation in both the frequency and ferocity of attacks.

### Mother ships

One interesting development as Somali piracy evolved was the trend for pirate action groups to move further away from the Somali coastline, dissipating into the wide expanses of sea, out of reach of the gathering naval assets. To operate far out into the Indian Ocean requires resources which the pirates do not have. As is their usual attitude, what they don't have, they simply take. This has led to an increased use of mother ships to facilitate attacks far out to sea.

Initially the pirates used old dhows and fishing vessels but on occasions would switch to using hijacked gas and chemical tankers to range the entire width of the Indian Ocean. This allowed the pirates to escalate their attacks but also negated the effects of the monsoon storms.

Mother ships have been taken by the pirates and usually have their own crew onboard as hostages. They are used to carry pirates, stores and fuel and often tow attack skiffs behind. If the mother ship is big enough, the skiffs may be carried onboard and camouflaged to prevent naval forces identifying them.

With increased naval capability, it seems the use of mother ships is currently on a downward trend. However, if pirates regain a foothold in their struggle with the military then it could be that they revisit this extremely effective tactic.

## Weaponry

Somali pirates are very adaptable, skilled and shrewd and there are concerns that there could be a shift to enhanced weapons. Pirates are not averse to investing in the tools of the trade and as many clans have invested ransom earnings into technology it may be the case that better boats, higher power engines and heavier weapons will be a natural consequence of their push to once again gain the upper hand.

Enhanced capability would enable the pirates to hit faster, harder and for longer.

Unconfirmed reports state that Somali pirates may be using the more advanced RPG-29 type rather than the less powerful RPG-7.

Somalia used to be a dumping ground for Russian arms back in the Cold War. Pirates use all types of weapons that they can get and these differ from region to region. Most of the weapons of the Somali pirates originate from the capital Mogadishu. They are Russian models, generally made in China, the Indian region or in Eastern European countries.

The AK-47 rifle was first issued to the Russian Army in 1949 and is still very popular because it is cheap, readily available and extremely reliable. Over 50M AK-47 or variants have been made worldwide.

The effective range is around 300-400m. Although the AK-47 is not particularly accurate, in skilled and experienced hands it can lay down sustained fire on a tight target area. Pirates have shown that even from an unstable platform the bridge windows are easy to hit, for instance.

Somali pirates place an enormous amount of reliance on their weapons. They use them in a challenging marine environment and yet are able to keep them working. Often when pirates take a vessel one of their first demands is for WD-40 or diesel so they can clean and maintain their weapons.

The RPG-7 was first issued to the troops of the Russian, Chinese and North Korean armies. It is readily available in arms markets.

The RPG-7 can hit a target at around 500m, but if the target is moving then it works best if the target is 300m or closer. These grenades can pierce through up to 30cm of armour and are popular choice of terrorists and pirates.

555

READ

The head of the RPG-7 shell is actually hollow. It works by punching a hole into the target. The charge then explodes and forces shrapnel inside the target. The usual steel accommodation on merchant vessels actually diminishes the effectiveness of the shells as there is a lesser weight of material to 'push' inwards, as opposed to an armoured target.

The RPG-29 anti-tank grenade recoilless launcher has an effective range of up to 500m, is single shot, smooth bored and fired from the shoulder.

Developed in Russia in the 1980s, the RPG-29 can penetrate the frontal armour of most modern tanks. It has been termed "the great equaliser" as it has a proven success rate against some of the most heavily-armoured tanks in the world. Second-hand models are now in circulation in the Middle East and security professionals fear that the Somalis will eventually use them. The destructive capability of the RPG-29 is being heralded as a potential tipping point in the waters off Somalia.

According to experts, when the more powerful RPGs are deployed a vessel's hull might be easily breached, with further damage, injury or even death incurred by the crew within. There is also increased scope for environmental damage if oil cargoes are breached and leak.

Casualties among ship crews would probably rise, armed private security contractors could be counteracted and pirates could even return fire on naval assets. The potential use of such weapons should be of the utmost concern.

To stop ships, pirates are increasingly looking to heavier weapons, such as the Russian SPG-9 recoilless gun or the DSHK 12.7mm heavy machine gun.

With these types of heavy machine gun they can take ships under fire from 2,000m and provide a substantial response to the fire of any private security services. Using such heavy machine guns, they could also take the helicopters of the international naval coalition.

The PK general purpose machine gun was designed in the Soviet Union and is currently in production in Russia. It was introduced in the 1960s and replaced the SGM and RPD machine guns in Soviet service. It remains in use as a front-line infantry to vehicle-mounted weapon with Russia's armed forces and has been exported extensively.

Firing rates vary from 650-850 rounds/minute (rpm), depending on the type used. There is an effective maximum range of approximately 1,000m.

The PK has been very popular as a weapon of the Libyan rebel forces mounted on the back of flatbed 4×4 vehicles. This machine gun frequently comes into the hands of pirates and is often used in hijack attacks as a support weapon.

The KPV heavy machine gun has been around for a long time and has become the popular choice of many terror organisations. This would suggest that pirate groups are aware of the weapon and of means to secure supplies, especially of the ZPU-1 variant. If pirates decide to increase their firepower, it is likely they would consider deck-mounting weapons such as KPVs to large skiffs or mother ships.

The KPV is capable of 450rpm, with an effective range of 1,500-2,000m. Compare this to the 300m range of an AK-47 and the problems for ships are obvious.

As armed shipboard teams have gained something of an upper hand, it is inevitable that as pirates grow more frustrated and desperate they will resort to an escalation in weaponry to increase their haul of hijacked vessels.

In mounting these heavier and more sophisticated weapons to their attack craft pirates may lose some speed and manoeuvrability. Many believe that the recoil and power when fired may mean that more pirates will end up in the water than has hitherto been the case.

The potential use of more powerful weapons with a greater range heightens the need to spot approaching pirates at an even greater distance. It has proved difficult enough when they have to get within 300m to fire but if they can extend their range and hit harder, the problems intensify.

# Other developments

### Stealth

Pirates have been using mother ships to launch highly visible decoy skiffs that approach the ship with the aim of drawing fire and attention. At the same time, pirates have moved towards the vessel in camouflaged skiffs trying to gain access on an unprotected side of the vessel.

### Swarming

Using a mother ship as a base, pirates have been able to swarm vessels with as many as 50 attackers. A small detachment of just four armed guards would inevitably struggle to maintain security in the face of such overwhelming odds.

### Masking

Pirates operating within more restricted waters, such as the southern Red Sea (off Eritrea) may be using local fishing fleets as cover.

The pirate skiffs remain in the vicinity of the fishing vessels and when a target ship approaches they accelerate from the fleet to approach and then attack.

### Children and youth in marine piracy

It is of increasing concern that many pirates arrested at sea appear to be under 18 years of age. When Indian authorities arrested a group of pirates, they were shocked to find that almost half of the 61 pirates they apprehended after a gun battle were children below the age of 15, with at least four thought to be aged 11.

It is appears to be a tragic fact that in countries blighted by war or terrorism children and young people are all too often coerced or seduced into criminality or conflict. It would perhaps be naïve to suppose that places such as Somalia would be any different.

The problem is a serious enough threat to warrant a special effort by the international community. The United Nations is working to counter this through its Office of the Special Representative of the Secretary-General for Children and Armed Conflict. Dalhousie University in Canada is the institutional home for the Roméo Dallaire Child Soldiers Initiative and has a major research and training focus on children and young people affected by conflict. However, it must be recognised that at sea it could be very difficult to accurately gauge the age of an attacker.

Pirates are likely to exploit this tactic further, as a means of bolstering their numbers for swarm attacks and to cause confusion in the ranks of the security teams.

With the application of the 100 series RUF, the guards, the ship's Master and shipping company can be assured they are responding in a reasonable, necessary and proportionate manner.

### Ship-to-ship transfers

As previously stated, the Western African brand of piracy is far faster, and perhaps harder hitting. Pirate gangs on this coast are not concerned with long drawn-out kidnaps for ransom but want to steal – whether cargoes, personal effects or cash.

Attacking in fast small vessels, they board and systematically embark on a sustained violent frenzy. These are terrifying, brutal and dangerous attacks.

Depending on their target, once on board they will steal what they have selected or will rendezvous with another vessel to transfer cargo (usually oil) during a ship-to-ship (STS) transfer. So swift and professional are these transfers that many questions have been raised about the actual identity of the gangs involved and of how they have been trained.

Whereas there have seemingly been some effective answers in tackling Somali piracy, the West African issue seems to be some way from a solution. The area has a mix of criminal gangs, corruption, instability, terrorism and petrochemical wealth. The riches to be made by stealing oil cargoes are driving ever greater levels of criminality at sea and seafarers and the shipping industry are suffering the consequences.

Image: The Security Association for the Maritime Industry (SAMI)

# Chapter 5

## Planning and practicalities

### KEY ADVICE

- Planning and preparation before entering the danger zone
- Understanding the importance of alertness and vigilance and managing fatigue
- Guidelines on watchkeeping and monitoring
- Guidelines on training, drills and exercises
- Understanding the physical interaction with small pirate craft
- Guidance on using the ship as a weapon of self-defence
- Guidance on access control and retreat to a citadel
- Understanding how to deal with a pirate attack

A voyage through high risk areas is not a normal one, making planning and understanding of what may be expected of the vessel vitally important. The BMP stress that reporting and responding correctly are essential to the pirate area transit.

Identifying suspicious craft at the earliest possible moment is vital to initiating a positive response. Such detection should trigger a response that demonstrates to attackers that they have been spotted.

Early indication of a pirate attack will enable the Master to respond appropriately to prevent boarding. It is vital that all on board understand the threat posed and are able to recognise an attack at the earliest possible stage and know what response is expected of them.

Ships that have successfully evaded pirates have spotted them early and had their response ready. To have a chance, it is essential to be alert and know what to do. For this reason, the possibility of fatigue should be carefully considered and crew monitored for signs.

Shipboard managers, supported by those ashore, should recognise the problem and put systems in place, or additional resources, to mitigate the risks posed to crew performance in the event of a pirate attack.

# Watchkeeping and monitoring

An effective watch must be kept and the look-out should be briefed on what to expect and the importance of spotting pirate skiffs early. Consideration should be given to reduced times spent on watch. Shorter sessions with increased breaks will help maintain vigilance.

Attackers will come in fast in very small craft. In heavy seas, they may be hard to spot, although small pirate skiffs rarely operate in conditions above sea state 5. However, some attacks have been known in rough conditions.

The fact that these are small targets, and are often hard to see, does not preclude the bridge team from taking all measures to ensure they are seen and identified. Additional watches on the stern or covering radar blind spots should be considered.

All available means of detection should be used in addition to visual watchkeeping. Pirate skiffs may be hard to spot by radar but it imperative that every effort is made to detect their presence. If targets are spotted moving at high speed and converging with the vessel, then it seems that an attack may be imminent and appropriate action should be taken.

A prompt and active response can prevent an attack and can certainly limit the pirates' chances of successful boarding. The OOW should be briefed to watch for small, fast targets and the radar set-up may take the need to observe such targets into account.

Traditional shipboard radars have been known to struggle with picking up small, fast, low targets. In fact failure to spot pirates in their skiffs has been seen as a major problem in securing vessels in the Gulf of Aden and Indian Ocean.

One answer has been the introduction of broadband radar, which boasts superior target definition and separation at close quarters – from a security perspective that is really what matters most.

Such systems enable watchkeepers to monitor important targets at ranges down to 1/32nm, while they can also expect 2-3m target resolution to 10nm with a maximum range of 24nm.

# Security duties

Many vessels operate with comparatively low crew numbers and this could severely restrict the ability of the crew to maintain increased watch patterns over a sustained period.

The CSO, Master and SSO should have been in discussion prior to entering the area and drawn up plans to make best use of the finite manning resources. It may be that other work has to stop over the period of the passage or that each department is utilised for patrolling and watchkeeping.

Traditional thinking has usually had increased patrolling at night in pirate areas. This may not be the most productive approach in this area, however, with Somali pirates known to prefer daylight raids.

However, consideration of lighting and night vision optics could be important where pirates switch tactics.

Alarms, intruder detection systems and CCTV are all useful tools. But in all but a few isolated cases, once the pirates have gained access to the vessel then it has been hijacked.

# Training and exercises

BMP state that crew training sessions should be conducted prior to transits, including citadel drills where utilised, and debriefing sessions after transits. The key to response is having trained on what to do and when. When a vessel is due to transit the HRA it is vital to train for the passage in order to ensure proper and effective action if an attack occurs.

Exercises and training could include drills to:

* Respond to attackers
* Call for assistance and practise communications
* Muster and/or withdraw personnel into a citadel
* Deal with pirates once they are on board
* Practise measures to manage hostage taking

The Master should brief all personnel of the dangers posed by the transit and of the measures to be implemented to mitigate the risks. All personnel should ensure they understand their duties and the means of fulfilling them.

# Defensive manoeuvres

With pirates attacking from small craft there have been Masters who have been able to protect their vessels by manoeuvring and using the vessel as a defensive tool. BMP stress the importance of practising such manoeuvres and understanding the positive use that can be made of interaction between the attacked vessel and pirate skiffs.

Masters should consider 'riding off' attacking craft by using heavy wheel movements as they approach. The effect of the bow wave and wash may deter attackers and make it difficult for them to attach poles, ladders or grappling irons to the ship.

Increased speed and evasive manoeuvring have prevented attacks. The success of such actions will vary according to the characteristics of the individual vessel. For example, the implications of such evasive actions for a tug and tow at 8kt are obviously not the same as for a container ship at 24kt.

Avoid making a lee for the pirate skiff. If possible try to get the wind and sea well forward of the beam on the weather side and try to keep the pirates on the weather side. This will make it harder for them to steady their skiffs, so they will find it more difficult to aim their weapons and get ladders hooked on.

All shipboard personnel should be warned to expect violent manoeuvres and should know how to protect themselves from slips, trips and falls owing to any sudden manoeuvres taken by the vessel.

Alterations of course can be an important part of the evasive manoeuvres but the implications for speed of any alterations should be remembered. Turning can slow the vessel down and may make it easier for the pirates to get closer to it.

When under attack it is important for a vessel to employ evasive manoeuvres. However, it also important to consider the hydrostatic effect and the role that interaction can play in ensuring pirate skiffs are unable to come alongside.

These hydrostatic elements move around a 'pivot point'. When making headway, as we would want to do if under attack, the forces experienced at a steady forward speed ensure the pivot point lies approximately one-quarter of the ship's length from forward.

When a ship is making headway, a positive pressure area builds up forward of the pivot point while aft of the pivot point the flow of water down the ship's side creates a low pressure area.

The positive pressure wave extends out from the ship and can act as a barrier to small craft trying to move closer to the vessel. However, further astern the low-pressure region acts as a 'suction' zone and affords some scope for small hostile craft to get close enough to attempt a boarding. The higher the speed of the vessel the greater the pressure exerted.

In normal operations, interaction has a detrimental effect. When used to help repel boarders it is an important defensive tool.

The development of positive pressure zones around the bow make it extremely difficult for pirate skiffs to manoeuvre closer to the vessel when attacking forward.

The positive bow pressure pushes the smaller vessel away. This effect will be short-lived, as once past the pivot point the smaller vessel will begin to be sucked inwards toward the target vessel.

It is important to note, therefore, that any defensive equipment is best situated astern of the pivot in the areas where small craft are most likely to be able to get close to their target.

# Access control

Measures to control access will be included in the SSP drawn up under the ISPS Code and are crucial in deterring or delaying pirates who have managed to board a vessel and are trying to enter accommodation or machinery spaces.

Watchkeepers on the wheelhouse, engine control room and deck should be fully briefed as to the risk of attack and the response expected of them and their fellow personnel.

Decks should be monitored regularly and additional watchkeeping arrangements made as appropriate. Deck watches should ensure their rounds demonstrate an active and alert presence around the vessel. Watchkeepers should ensure they are in contact with the OOW and report in at regular intervals.

Watchkeepers should:

- Make rounds
- Keep moving
- Create a highly visible presence
- Conduct frequent but irregular patrol patterns around the vessel
- Have a checklist to follow

- Be briefed as to what they are looking for and what to do if they detect suspicious activity

Pirate attacks are taking place against moving vessels, so gangways and hull openings are likely to be closed and stowed. It is important, however, to ensure easy access is prevented and that no items that pirates could make use of (such as tools) are lying around the deck or in unlocked storage.

The BMP contains much useful information on self-protection measures, including protecting areas such as doorways, portholes and bridge windows. There is also a section on the use of water and foam monitors and of citadels. Advice issued in the past included the use of fire hoses which put crews in danger. New advice is now available on the best use of water and foam and of alternative ways of delivering it to protect the vessel.

# Citadels

Much attention has been given to the concept of citadels within the maritime media and BMP.

A citadel as defined in BMP is "a designated pre-planned area purpose-built into the ship where, in the event of imminent boarding by pirates, all crew will seek protection. A citadel is designed and constructed to resist a determined pirate trying to gain entry for a fixed period of time".

There have been an increasing number of occasions where crews have foiled pirates because they could not gain access to the vessel or individual crew members.

The growth in use has prompted the shipping industry to produce a set of guidelines on the construction and use of citadels in waters affected by Somalia piracy. The document has received approval from Round Table members (Intertanko, BIMCO, ICS and Intercargo) as well as other industry associations. NATO, EU NAVFOR and the Combined Maritime Force (CMF) have also approved the document.

The content of the guidance is restricted but shipping companies will be able to access the information through the relevant trade association.

Citadels have proved to be successful in a number of attacks, but there have also been instances in which they have been breached. These may be attributed to a number of factors, including poor construction and location of the citadel. Pirates have also gained experience in defeating citadels using weapons and ship-board tools, smoking out crews and setting fire to vessels.

If designed and managed effectively a citadel can be a significant and important security asset. However, if the necessary requirements are not in place it could actually endanger the lives of those onboard. As such it is vital that a citadel is properly established and its use planned.

# Preparing a citadel

It is strongly recommended that citadels are seen as complementary to, rather than a replacement for, all other self-protection measures. NATO has been quick to stress that it remains the responsibility of owners, operators and Masters to decide and implement policy in relation to the use of citadels. It also stresses that the use of a citadel does not guarantee a military response.

Before owners, operators and Masters commit to a policy that recommends the use of a citadel, it is important to understand the criteria that military forces will apply before boarding to free the ship can be considered:

- 100% of the crew must be secured in the citadel
- The crew of the ship must have self-contained, independent, two-way external communications. Sole reliance on VHF communications is insufficient
- The pirates must be denied access to propulsion

The following points should also be taken into consideration:

- All emergency equipment in the citadel should be fully and regularly tested for functionality
- The communications system should have a power supply for a minimum of five days, based on a continuous open line
- A full list of emergency contact numbers, including UKMTO, should be held inside the citadel
- At least five days stock of food, water and provisions for all the crew should be available in the citadel
- Medical supplies, including medication for the treatment of physical trauma, and sanitation should be made available
- Provision of lifesaving and fire-fighting apparatus within the citadel

It is important to remember that the use of a citadel, even where the criteria are applied, cannot guarantee a naval or military response. This is explicit within the BMP.

There is a considerable degree of misunderstanding of the citadel concept in merchant shipping. To fully understand the rationale behind the concept it is important to consider its origin on naval vessels.

The citadel concept stems from the military need to ensure survivability of the vessel and this prompted naval architects to examine every system and function of a warship, determining which functions and systems are critical (and in what priority) to its survival and mission accomplishment. This analysis led to designs in which all vital systems and functions are located in a single area within the hull of the vessel – an 'armoured citadel'. In and beneath this, the propulsion plant, communications systems, weapons, ammunition stores and command and control of the ship resided.

Taking this basic idea and translating it as a retrofit onto merchant vessels is not easy. To construct a true citadel and ensure the crew are trained to use it effectively is not a simple task.

# Under attack

When an attack is deemed to be imminent, the security plans need to be followed. A Mayday should be sent, the SSAS initiated and all steps taken to defend the vessel and call for urgent assistance.

If a vessel suspects that it is coming under a pirate attack, there are specific actions that are recommended to be taken during the approach stage and the attack stage. If not already at full speed when being approached, increase to maximum. Steer a straight course to maintain a maximum speed.

The communication plan at this time is vital. In addition to previous advice BMP state that once established, communication with UKMTO should be maintained. The advice also states that attacks should be reported to UKMTO even if the vessel is part of a national convoy so other merchant ships can be warned.

The issue of ballistic protection is a key element of the BMP guidance. When under attack it is stressed that all crew except those required on the bridge should muster at the Safe Muster Point (or citadel if constructed), so that the crew are given as much ballistic protection as possible should the pirates get close enough to use weapons.

BMP state that Kevlar jackets and helmets (preferably in non-military colours) should be available for the bridge team. When the attack starts, the advice is to ensure that all external doors and, where possible, internal public rooms and cabins, are fully secured.

In addition to the emergency alarms and announcement for the benefit of the vessel's crew, the ship's whistle or foghorn should be sounded continuously to demonstrate to any potential attacker that the ship is aware of the attack and is reacting to it.

At this phase it is important to reconfirm that all ship's personnel are in a position of safety. As the pirates close on the vessel, Masters should commence small alterations of helm while maintaining a speed to deter skiffs from lying alongside the vessel in preparation for a boarding attempt. These manoeuvres will create additional wash to impede the operation of the skiffs.

It is stressed that substantial amounts of helm are not recommended, as these are likely to significantly reduce a vessel's speed.

# If boarded

If the worst does happen and the ship is boarded by pirates, the BMP state it is essential to try to remain calm and not escalate matters further. There comes a point when further resistance is not just futile but could also mean increased risk of injury to personnel and possible retribution by the pirates.

The pirates are likely to be aggressive, highly agitated and possibly under the influence of drugs, such as khat; shipboard personnel should be aware of the risk of violence and try to avoid heightening an already tense situation.

If the pirates do manage to board and take control of the vessel, the guidance currently states that the SSAS should be activated, the AIS should be switched on and any CCTV cameras should be left recording.

The Master and command team should ensure that they are able to issue orders to personnel to desist from further attempts to repel the attackers.

The attack now moves into a new phase and the response of shipboard personnel must also adapt to best ensure their own safety. The actions of the ship's crew may be fuelled by aggression and adrenaline during the attack. Now in the defence phase behaviour should be tempered. There is a risk that in close proximity to the attackers who have taken over the vessel things could escalate.

The Master and senior officers should consider ways of reassuring and calming their personnel and relaxing the atmosphere once it is clear that the vessel has been taken and there is nothing further they can do to defend it. This is not easy to do but can be vital in ensuring that casualties are minimised.

# Chapter 6
## Hostages

### KEY ADVICE

- Understanding how to respond to a successful boarding
- Understanding ways of minimising violence
- Understanding the negotiation process
- Managing a hijack
- Understanding how to respond to military action
- Managing the freed vessel
- Understanding the importance of post-incident reporting

If pirates do gain control of the vessel, relationship management is crucially important. Masters, CSOs and SSOs should be aware of their responsibilities and of what they can actually do to lessen the risk to their crew and ensure that they are as comfortable as possible when hostages. They need to know how to help crew pass the time and remain positive.

The pirates have taken the crew and vessel in order to obtain ransom money, meaning the crew are worth more alive than dead. This is an important point to remember. The captives should ensure they do nothing to provoke a violent response from the pirates. It is important to keep a survival attitude.

## Lessons learnt from past piracy hostage taking

### Remain positive

The vast majority of pirate captives survive – the odds are good. However, personnel should prepare for a long captivity. Many hostages have been held for months but it is vital to keep a positive attitude and take one day at a time.

Once the ship is taken, personnel become part of a business transaction. It may be difficult but hostages should try to relax and remember that many different people will be working tirelessly to bring about their release.

Remaining calm, positive, strong and focused can make all the difference. While it is easy to say this, it is much harder to do in the stress being taken hostage. Trying to maintain this mental attitude, approach and demeanour can help those captured to come through the ordeal.

**Keep relaxed**

Most pirate gangs rotate the personnel they put onboard the vessel. After the boarding gang have left the vessel they will most likely be placed in the control of a holding gang.

These new pirates may not be as volatile or as violent as the grab gang, so it may be possible to explore some sort of coexistence onboard in order to minimise aggression and hostility.

It is important to cooperate (within reason) and not to make threats or become violent. Apart from very rare instances, attempts to escape have been futile and have prompted a harsh response and retribution.

**Keep your dignity**

According to research, it is generally psychologically harder for a person to kill or otherwise harm a captive if they remain human in the captor's eyes. So crews are advised not to grovel, beg or become hysterical.

It is also important to try to resist challenging the pirates and to avoid entering into physical conflict.

**Coping with torture**

Of most concern is the treatment of seafarers held. For a long time there was an impression (whether real or imagined), that pirates were abiding by a form of pirate code. They avoided ill treatment and most captives were eventually released unharmed.

There is a frightening trend away from this almost quaint vision – and increasingly there are reports of torture and ill treatment of captives.

As the stakes and the pressure mount, it seems that Somali pirate groups are becoming much harder in their attitude towards the seafarers they hold. It is important that the industry makes it clear that this is not a case of seafarers getting taken and then simply sitting around until they are freed – the game has changed, and now their lives are in danger.

Captive crews need to become adept at assessing the threats posed by the pirates holding them. Some may treat them in an acceptable manner, while others may become vicious or agitated.

There is no clear means of dealing with such violence and the use of these tactics but being aware of this trend is important. Perhaps the best means of coping is to try to manage relations with the pirates so as to avoid potential violent flashpoints.

# Negotiations

Once captured, most vessels are taken back to the Somali coast and their crews held in appalling conditions off the coastal towns.

The average length of time hostages spend in captivity while lawyers, negotiators, agents and local fixers negotiate over the price of release has increased and is now close to eight months.

Suzanne Williams, an experienced negotiator, gives an outline of the negotiation process.

*When maritime hostages are taken, the complete inclusive negotiation package must include the safe release of all the crew, vessel and sometimes the cargo. An agreement for safe passage away from the area is also a crucial dimension of the settlement.*

*The logistics of the ransom delivery have to be agreed in great detail, therefore, leaving no surprises for either side. At this closing stage of administration rather than negotiation, the crisis responder will require timely decision-making and leadership from the crisis management team and responsible, steady behaviour from the crew.*

*Negotiation is not just about money. It requires more discipline and structure and conclusion is not simply a matter of price reduction or bartering. It is a process which builds a rapport, trust and the need for an understanding of previous business arrangements. In cases of piracy this process does not happen quickly, although, things tend to speed up once the money becomes a reality. Both parties should heed the words of the late Lord King (an ex-chairman of British Airways): "The most dangerous time in any negotiation is when you think that you are winning."*

*To date, the motivation of modern day pirates has been solely a financial one. There has not yet been maritime hostage-taking for ideological reasons or blatant acts of terrorism. Should this criminal motivation change, more expressive negotiation strategies would have to be deployed that would demand a more diverse response drawing on the assistance of many external international influences.*

*Successful negotiation with the pirates requires long-term contacts, a good non-judgmental understanding of both events and the necessary response. Only then is there hope to bring about a temporary solution to these acts of human suffering, one case at a time. The traditional negotiator's training and toolbox of tested tactics commonly used in sieges, bank robberies and barricades are not necessarily going to achieve the desired outcome with the pirates. To them it is a business; therefore the negotiation should mirror the style of communication in board rooms rather than megaphones on the street.*

*This is a serious business; remember that whoever is doing the talking does so against the backdrop of people's lives being in their hands. It is not a job for the faint-hearted but only for those who are committed to bringing about a safe and speedy release.*

## Managing a hijack

When a vessel is pirated and the crew kidnapped for ransom management of events will be long and complex. BIMCO has been a leader in preparing its members for the problems they may face and has provided guidance from capture to release.

It is vital that the full process is considered and that the company facing negotiations with pirates has anticipated the problems it may face. The following key elements should be addressed as a minimum:

**Procedures** – This is not a time for guesswork, so robust, workable and effective procedures must be laid down in advance

**Training** – It is vital that systems are checked and training has been implemented

**First alerts** – The process will move quickly and it is important to know how the first alerts will be handled and how the response will be escalated

**Negotiations** – If trading in a high risk area, the company should have already considered the potential for attack and hijack. It would be useful to have already identified the negotiation process and the personnel charged with this task (whether in-house or externally sourced)

**Families –** The Maritime Piracy Humanitarian Response Programme (MPHRP) has developed training courses and established some best practice for companies to follow. They encourage shipping companies to have a dedicated family liaison role.

This position can provide a vitally important focal point for the families and help to maintain positive relations. However, there is some criticism of using a shipping company employee in this role and it may be that an independent person could be better placed to ensure that trust is maintained between the affected parties.

**Media –** Managing the media is an important part of the overall process. If the media is not handled properly this can lead to immense problems throughout the process of trying to free the vessel. Companies are encouraged to have access to professional media expertise, either to liaise and limit exposure or to manage stories when they appear.

Media management is a real issue when considering hostage taking; pirates do understand the media so where possible the expert advice is to deny the media information, as exposure can affect agreed settlement. Pirates want to get to the families if they can find them and use them to bring pressure to owners, and the media is a tool for this.

Understand that disgruntled or disaffected family members or stakeholders may turn to the media if they do not feel sufficient progress is being made to free the hostages.

**Social media –** The same can also be said of social media. When seafarers are taken hostage, companies should have a means of working with families to ensure that privacy settings on social networks are increased.

According to hostage negotiators, social networking is changing the initial responses. They are having to accept that families want and need to communicate, so it has been suggested that setting up secure "chat" facilities can assist the process by keeping families connected yet denying access to external parties.

**Ransom delivery –** How is this to be done and by whom?

# Immediate action ashore

**Crisis management** – The team ashore must be ready to react and have all the information and equipment necessary to be able to communicate and access all necessary resources

**Implement agreed strategy with all stakeholders** – Contact should be instigated with necessary parties and they should be reassured that the company is ready to manage the incident. There will be legal and insurance considerations, and all should be briefed

**Inform and update families** – The issue of families is a key concern. All necessary measures should be taken to ensure they are cared for and their concerns answered. It is likely that the families will be in countries far from the company, so it is important that a localised response is provided

**Negotiations** – It is important to use professional negotiators. It is vital that the Master onboard is only used as a facilitator, not a negotiator

**Single point of contact** – A single point of contact should be established to aid the process and this should not necessarily be the most senior company employee. The CEO or MD will be required to make tough calls and decisions, so it could be sensible to have that role free to perform the necessary oversight

**Media plan** – What should be said to who and when? Basically, the press are likely to be sympathetic if they are briefed and as long as they see that all is being done to facilitate a swift conclusion. It is important that the media are involved and understand what is going on

**Communications plan and control** – Again the process of communication has to be managed and this is not just about what is being said, but how. There are technical as well as planning issues

# Continuing crisis management

Once the initial hijack has taken place, there is a requirement to keep stakeholders informed and ensure that there is a clear and managed process so that the company can deliver all that is necessary.

**Regular contact with families** – Having established a local contact, it is important that a schedule of contact is maintained. The families will be going through a range of emotions, from initial acceptance to trust in the company, through to anger and upset. They need to be reassured

**Implementation of media plan** – Having developed a plan, this needs to be managed and monitored. There will probably be a period of grace from the media in which they accede to requests for time to get the response in place. If they feel there is no plan or that the crew are suffering, there is likely to be a backlash

**Avoid direct media contact with crew** – The pirates have often chosen to push the media by making demands to them and by putting obviously confused and distressed crew members in touch with the media. This is hard to manage but the crew should be constantly assured that the company is doing all it can and that talking to the media may jeopardise their release

**Negotiations** – Use of professional negotiators should mean that a consistent presence is possible

**Regular contact with kidnappers** – Negotiators should be doing what they believe is correct. However, the company should monitor the level of contact

**Beware of ruses** – The pirates may well try to trick the company into payment and there are usually a number of other people involved in the negotiation. Companies should do all possible to ensure they are dealing with genuine people who have the links necessary to get the vessel freed

**Knowledge of processes and trends** – The company should be provided with the insight necessary through its use of professional negotiators

**Prepared counter-offers and strategies** – The negotiation team should be able to handle such issues and remain focused on the end game of getting the vessel and crew safely out

# The role of the Master and crew

Once under the control of the pirates, communication with the Master and crew will be limited or difficult. This heightens the importance of training prior to transit of the HRA. Shipboard personnel should be prepared for the realities of hijack and should know what is expected of them, the best ways to increase the likelihood of survival and also of the efforts which the company will be making to ensure they are freed.

An increasing number of shipping companies now provide training to crews and their anti-piracy training also encompasses techniques for dealing with the realities of being held hostage.

Those onboard should be trained to concentrate on survival and how to best to ensure this. The key element is leadership onboard and the crew should try to work together to ensure that there is a common and unified sense of purpose.

There will be intense pressure onboard and the crew must do all possible to ensure that working and personal relationships onboard do not get too fraught.

It is easy to say that all onboard should avoid panic but this is perhaps a very natural state. While it may be hard to remain calm, the crew should try to focus on the positive actions they can take to survive. Avoiding panic may not be wholly realistic, so perhaps instead personnel should be encouraged to re-focus this heightened state and use the anxiety to ensure that they are working hard to do the right things.

Be prepared for extended captivity. While the company will be working hard to ensure as swift a release as possible, the sad fact remains that the crew could be held for an extended length of time – it is common for hostages to be held for more than 150 days. Freeing captives is about the long haul and a sustained period of fear, depression and uncertainty. Crews should be encouraged to try to maintain a degree of discipline and routine.

Crews that are taken hostage need to work together as a unified group. The strength that this can bring may be vital over the weeks, even months, of captivity.

Stay neutral. Anger is inevitable and there will be resentment too, but crews should be equipped with awareness to encourage them to remain neutral. Hostage-taking is not personal and they should be encouraged to see this as a problem which will end if they are able to simply see out their time.

Perhaps the most important mantra is to take one day at a time. Keep alive for the day, and then do the same again the next, and the next – until the vessel is eventually freed. Eat enough food, get enough water, keep free of disease, stay optimistic and help your fellow crew members for one day, every day, until the ordeal is over.

# Preparations for release

**Logistics of ransom delivery** – Even before a deal is done, the company should know the options available for delivering the ransom. There is no point haggling for weeks or months only to then have the problem of getting the cash delivered. This could set the process back significantly.

**Attention to crew** – In readying the vessel for release, the crew has to be considered. Crew members need to slowly change their mindset from the steady, one day at a time view which has kept them alive to a new approach of readying themselves to get their vessel gone and clear.

**Medical needs** – Are there any immediate medical concerns? If so, what are they and who is affected? If all of the bridge team are ill, or all the engineers incapacitated, this could be significant and will affect the release.

**Trauma considerations** – What about the state of mind of the crew? Are they ready, willing and able to sail the vessel once more?

**Resupply of the ship** – If the crew are ready, is the ship able to proceed? What about bunkers, provisions or repairs? If urgent resupply is necessary, how and when can this be done? What are the options for running the vessel low on fuel or water?

**Routeing to a safe haven** – Where is the nearest and most appropriate port to proceed for? The closest, however, may not always be the best. If there are serious casualties onboard, would it be better to get them to a port with adequate medical facilities? Or is it better to dock the vessel safely and get the necessary services to them? This should be planned in advance and contingency options arrived at.

**Military assistance** – Military forces are unlikely to be willing to step in unless the vessel is in danger, so there should be no reliance on military intervention once the vessel is freed. However, it is important to ensure that the naval assets are aware of what is happening and the company should establish a chain of communication with the appropriate authorities.

# Post-release

**Fast return to safe waters** – There needs to be a management process to handle where the vessel should head and the vessel needs to be moved quickly and safely to a secure location. The Master should know where is considered safe and should make best speed to reach safety, notwithstanding the need to manage the resources onboard and the state of the vessel.

**Medical attention provided** – There are likely to be casualties onboard, whether directly injured by pirates or as a result of neglect or lack of food. Medical advisors should be on hand to advise. The medical needs should have been identified prior to release and a plan should be in place to ensure that any medicines or treatment can be provided at the earliest possible moment.

**Well-being of the crew** – Care of the crew is paramount and once they have reached safety the danger posed to them is not over. Far from it, while they may not be in immediate danger, there are many considerations which should be given over to their care.

**Post-traumatic stress** – Some injuries are obvious but while cuts, wounds and physical illness can be readily identified and treated, it should be remembered that many of the ship's personnel might be suffering some degree of post-traumatic stress disorder (PTSD). For this reason, the company would be encouraged to ensure personnel receive both medical treatment and counselling after any hostage event or serious attack. Such considerations should also be provided to families, as they too will have suffered greatly. There should also be plans in place to deal with the ramifications of any deaths suffered and the company should look to ensure that families are cared for. It may also be that shore-based staff are suffering the ill effects of what can be a sustained period of intense and stressful activity and their needs should also be considered.

**Preservation of evidence** – With an increased focus on bringing pirates to justice, there is a need to preserve evidence and crews should be trained in what they should be doing. Once freed, the company should have a systematic approach to detailing the necessary information.

**Debriefings and reports** – Once the process is completed, the vessel is freed, evidence is gathered and the crew (and families) are receiving the necessary medical and psychological support, then the company should begin to close out the incident by means of reports, learning lessons and debriefs to ship and shore staff.

BMP derives from reports sent from vessels and the experiences of the industry. In order to develop a body of knowledge and to improve response, it is vital that reports are generated and issued. Post-incident reporting is a vital step to closing out any incident.

This reporting will enable future updates to BMP and it is important that vessels are in possession of the latest edition.

# Military action

There have been an increasing number of attempts by military agents to release vessels held, making it essential that crews are ready and know what to do in the event of a release attempt.

This is about keeping your head down (quite literally). Masters, CSOs and SSOs should ensure that personnel know that their lives could be in very real danger if they do not follow some common sense steps. They should not take photos and should comply with any instructions issued by the military.

BMP provides advice in the event of military action: "On no account should personnel make movements which could be misinterpreted as being aggressive".

It is also stressed that while the military will endeavour to respond rapidly to acts of piracy, because of the very large distances across the HRA a military response may not be possible.

Military forces have stressed that the preparation of a released vessel is not a task for them and that companies are responsible for their own vessels. This includes the provision of fuel and other necessary supplies to enable the ship to go to its intended next port.

While this stance will obviously not preclude warships from providing assistance to any vessel in distress or in need of aid, as mandated by the SOLAS, or humanitarian support if positioned to do so, it is an important part of any ship and company plan to consider how to manage that first post-release transit.

Once the vessel is freed and proceeds on its way the normal hazards of a transit apply.

# Chapter 7
## Tackling piracy

### KEY ADVICE

- Understanding efforts to counter piracy and the issues arising
- Assessing key developments
- Assessing potential piracy solutions

With the escalation in piracy off the coast of Somalia, the European Union under the Common Security Defence Policy (CSDP) launched a naval operation to protect humanitarian aid and reduce the attacks on shipping in the region.

The military operation, called EU NAVFOR Somalia – Operation ATALANTA, was launched in support of Resolutions 1814, 1816, 1838 and 1846 adopted in 2008 by the United Nations Security Council (UNSC). Resolution 1918 followed in 2009 and EU NAVFOR is currently operating under UNSCR 1950 (2010). Its specific aims are:

- Protection of vessels of the World Food Programme delivering food aid to displaced persons in Somalia
- Protection of vulnerable vessels cruising off the Somali coast and the deterrence, prevention and repression of acts of piracy and armed robbery off that coast
- Monitoring of fishing activities off the coast of Somalia

The operation was scheduled for an initial period of 12 months but it has been subsequently extended by the EU Council and is now authorised until December 2014. The funding of EU NAVFOR ATALANTA has amounted to in excess of €8M annually since its inception.

This budget is shared between the EU member states, based on their GDP, and covers the financing of common costs, such as the Operational Headquarters (Northwood, UK), the force headquarters (onboard the flagship) and medical services and transport.

Costs of supplying military assets and personnel are shared by the contributing states according to their involvement in the operation, with each state bearing the cost of the resources it deploys. By December 2010, 26 countries had contributed in varying degrees to the operation. The breakdown is as follows:

- 13 EU member states provided an operational contribution to EU NAVFOR, either with ships, with maritime patrol and reconnaissance aircraft, or with vessel protection detachment (VPD) team. This included France, Spain, Germany, Greece, Sweden, Netherlands, Italy, Belgium, the UK (also hosting the EU NAVFOR operational headquarters), Portugal, Luxembourg, Malta and Estonia.

- Nine other EU member states participated in the effort, providing military staff to work at the EU NAVFOR operational headquarters (Northwood, UK) or onboard units. These are Cyprus, Romania, Bulgaria, Slovenia, Czech Republic, Hungary, Poland, Ireland and Finland

- Four non-EU member states (Norway, Croatia, Ukraine and Montenegro) have so far also brought their contribution to EU NAVFOR. Norway has also provided an operational contribution with a warship regularly deploying in the area of operation

The force size fluctuates according to the monsoon seasons, which determine the level of piracy. It typically consists of five-10 surface combatants, one to two auxiliary ships and two to four maritime patrol and reconnaissance aircraft. It operates in a zone comprising the south of the Red Sea, the Gulf of Aden and the western part of the Indian Ocean including the Seychelles, which represents an area of 2M nm$^2$ (almost 4M km$^2$).

EU NAVFOR increased its area of operations in September 2010 to maintain pressure on the pirates and to continue to constrain their freedom of action.

Given the size of the area to be policed, there is no feasible way that sufficient presence can effectively be brought to bear. Even at speeds of 30kt there is a minuscule operational footprint for naval vessels and capability is only boosted marginally when aircraft are brought into the mix.

It has been quoted that it would take 83 helicopter-equipped vessels to provide an effective one-hour response. Given that most attacked vessels are only able to request help with around 10mins warning, the problems are clear.

# Legal issues

The maritime force can arrest, detain and transfer persons who have committed, or are suspected of having committed, acts of piracy or armed robbery in the areas where it is present. It can seize the vessels of the pirates or armed robbers or the vessels caught following an act of piracy or an armed robbery and which are in the hands of the pirates, as well as the goods on board.

All pirates will be tried in accordance with international human rights standards to guarantee that no one shall be subjected to the death penalty, to torture or to any cruel, inhuman or degrading treatment.

Although the issue of how and where to deal with pirates is a continuing concern, and despite trials in neighbouring states to Somalia and high profile actions in the US and Europe, the answer to the problem of bringing pirates to justice has not yet been solved completely.

# Results

Since escorts began in late 2007, not a single ship carrying WFP food to ports in Somalia has been attacked by pirates. Under the EU NAVFOR operation, which started in December 2008, and up to November 2010, WFP has delivered more than 480,000 tonnes of food into Somalia through Mogadishu, Merka, Bossaso, Berbera ports.

There has also been a high degree of success in breaking up pirate action groups. However, it seems that the battle against piracy is far from over as the pirates move further out into the Indian Ocean to find target vessels away from the umbrella of naval protection.

# Hard or soft options

With the navies of many nations massed off the coast of Somalia and in the Gulf of Aden, differences have emerged in the responses of certain nations.

The Special Forces of the US, South Korea and Malaysia have all been involved in aggressive responses to pirates – operations which thankfully were comparatively successful.

The US rescue of Captain Richard Phillips from the lifeboat of his vessel *Maersk Alabama* will long be the stuff of legend and Hollywood too. The Malaysian operation resulted in three of the seven pirates who attacked that vessel wounded and the crew of 23 freed without harm. The South Korean operation on a third vessel resulted in eight of the 13 pirates onboard the tanker killed and the others taken prisoner. The ship's crew of 21 was safe but the captain was shot in the stomach by a pirate, although he survived.

The use of such force has called into the question the attitude of some nations to simply maintaining an almost 'watching brief', while vessels are hijacked or individuals are shipped back to the Somali mainland.

While force obviously has its advantages there are some, including the IMB and EU NAVFOR, that recommend a more cautious approach when considering engaging in armed assault of pirated ships. It seems that if a vessel is taken, there can be a significant difference in the response of any naval assets in the vicinity. Any over-reliance on the so-called cavalry rescue approach is deemed to be misguided.

## Piracy and the ISPS Code

Some have seen the very need for BMP as admission that the provisions of the ISPS Code were either lacking or have not worked.

There may be some truth in this but it should be remembered that all the provisions of the BMP can and should be built into the SSP and the requirements to manage security risks and react to them have been there all along. It is perhaps only with the pressure created by this new wave of modern piracy that many have seen a real role for security.

All too often the demands of ISPS seemed able to deal only with 'soft' security threats such as checking passenger tickets or searching baggage. A disconnect arose between the protection that security can provide and the means of delivering it. Now with this threat in the Indian Ocean there is a real need to better protect vessels and systems and mechanisms are in place to provide real security that will be robust in the face of determined and violent attackers.

## Non-commercial shipping

The Somali pirate attacks also impact on yachting and leisure activities. The NATO Shipping Centre advises yachts not to sail through the Gulf of Aden and the Somali Basin. Several international authorities and the International Sailing Federation have also warned about the danger of piracy in the Gulf of Aden, Yemeni and Somali waters.

NATO has re-iterated that coalition counter-piracy forces are not in a position to afford dedicated protection for these vessels.

Any yachts already in the vicinity or intending to travel in this area, despite the advice not to go there, should inform MSCHOA by emailing postmaster@mschoa.org, with the subject line Yacht Vessel Movement and read the guidance on the homepages of MSCHOA and the NATO Shipping Centre (www.mschoa.org, www.shipping.nato.int).

## IMO: orchestrating the response

Since 2011, the IMO has concentrated on orchestrating the response to piracy. Efforts follow these key objectives, with support from associated UN agencies to:

- Increase pressure at the political level to secure the immediate release of hostages being held by pirates
- Review, with the aim of updating and improving the long-established guidelines to the industry while seeking to promote, to the fullest extent possible, the recommended preventive, evasive and defensive measures that ships sailing through piracy-infested areas should comply with
- Seek wider and better coordinated support from navies
- Seek to promote better cooperation and coordination between and among states, regions and organisations
- Intensify efforts to build the capacity of states (especially those that lie close to affected areas) to deter, interdict and bring to justice those who commit acts of piracy and armed robbery against ships
- Take action to ensure that those attacked or hijacked by pirates and their families receive support and social care

## The Djibouti Code of Conduct

In January 2009, an important regional agreement was adopted in Djibouti by states in the region, at a high-level meeting convened by IMO.

*The Code of Conduct concerning the Repression of Piracy and Armed Robbery against Ships in the Western Indian Ocean and the Gulf of Aden* (the Djibouti Code of Conduct) was drawn up to highlight the extent of the maritime security problems in the region. The signatories declared their intention to cooperate to the fullest possible extent, and in a manner consistent with international law, in the repression of piracy and armed robbery against ships.

The Code involved commitments to:

● Share and report relevant information through a system of national focal points and information centres
● Allow and engage in the interdiction of ships suspected of engaging in acts of piracy or armed robbery against ships
● Ensure that persons committing or attempting to commit acts of piracy or armed robbery against ships are apprehended and prosecuted
● Facilitation of proper care, treatment and repatriation for seafarers, fishermen, other shipboard personnel and passengers subject to acts of piracy or armed robbery against ships, particularly those who have been subjected to violence

Implementation of the Djibouti Code of Conduct aims to:

● Improve communications between states
● Enhance the capabilities of states in the region to deter, arrest and prosecute pirates
● Improve states' maritime situational awareness
● Enhance the capabilities of local coast guards
● Enhance the awareness of industry best management practice
● Assist in garnering additional support from states able to provide warships and maritime patrol aircraft for the Gulf of Aden and Western Indian Ocean area
● Assist in bringing Maritime Rescue Co-ordination Centres in Mombasa and Dar-es-Salaam into a more evolved counter-piracy role

In the longer term, the IMO is seeking to promote international action to stabilise the situation in Somalia through the UN Security Council, the UN Political Office for Somalia, the UN Development Programme, the Contact Group on Piracy off Somalia, and others. There is a very real sense that the situation off Somalia, will only be resolved in the long term by solutions brought about ashore.

The signatory states of the Djibouti Code are currently Comoros, Djibouti, Egypt, Eritrea, Ethiopia, Jordan, Kenya, Madagascar, Maldives, Mauritius, Mozambique, Oman, Saudi Arabia, Seychelles, Somalia, South Africa, Sudan, United Arab Emirates, United Republic of Tanzania, and Yemen.

## Shared Awareness and Deconfliction

The SHADE meeting was established in December 2008 to coordinate the efforts of the numerous military forces conducting counter-piracy in the region. Tactical and operational commanders meet with their counterparts to provide awareness of current and planned operations, discuss threat analysis, and provide feedback to the Contact Group for Piracy off the Coast of Somalia (created in January 2009 pursuant to UN Security Council Resolution 1851).

At the latest meeting in May 2011, 108 representatives from the militaries of 28 countries, law enforcement agencies, the shipping industry and various governments met in Bahrain to discuss counter-piracy operations in the Gulf of Aden and the Somali Basin.

SHADE meets regularly in Bahrain, which is the home of the Combined Maritime Forces. Through regular coordination meetings, the militaries have gained valuable insight in countering the threat of piracy to global shipping.

## Potential piracy solutions

A number of key nations are beginning to assess some radical proposals and changes to their anti-piracy strategies.

The Dutch government has announced plans to allow its navy to attack pirates on Somali territory, using the existing EU piracy mandate to perform pre-emptive strikes ashore.

Several other nations have amended, or are in the process of reviewing, their policies to recognise that engaging armed personnel should be an option for their shipowners to combat piracy.

Other developments have emerged from the US, as it looks to use lessons learned from battling drug barons and terrorists. The US has been spurred by what it sees as a vicious cycle in which ever-rising ransom payments mean not just further piracy but also increased pirate capabilities and sophistication. The carrot of ransoms has created a stick with which the pirates are beating us. Piracy has gone from a fairly ad hoc disorganised criminal endeavour to a highly developed transnational criminal enterprise.

This evolution has prompted the US to recognise that piracy can only be effectively addressed through "broad, coordinated, and comprehensive international efforts". This has prompted what the US terms a "multi-dimensional approach", focusing on security, prevention and deterrence.

Many experts support the belief that there must be a focus on parallel security efforts ashore. Indeed, many believe that "the battles may be won at sea, but the war will be won on land". The US approach has been to expand prosecution and incarceration. When suspected pirates have been captured, the US has consistently pushed affected states to take responsibility to try suspects and incarcerate them if convicted.

More than 1,000 pirates are in custody in more than 18 countries where national prosecutions are taking place. Catch and release does not work, so proper, effective sanctions must be in place.

The US intends to supplement naval actions at sea with targeting of pirate leaders and organisers ashore to disrupt the activities of the financiers, organisers and logistics suppliers who make piracy possible.

Arrest and prosecution of pirates captured at sea, often low-level operatives, is insufficient on its own to meet the longer-term counter-piracy goals. Pirate leaders and facilitators receive income both from investors and ransom payments and disburse a portion of the proceeds of ransoms back to their investors and to the pirates who hijack the ships and hold the crews hostage.

The US will focus on identifying and apprehending the criminal conspirators who provide the leadership and financial management and has recently indicted and extradited two alleged Somali pirate negotiators for their respective leadership roles in the attack on the *Quest*.

To break the criminal cycle, the US is working to connect law enforcement communities, intelligence agencies, financial experts and international partners to promote information sharing and develop actionable information against pirate conspirators. This effort includes tracking pirate sources of financing and supplies, such as fuel, outboard motors and weapons. Finally, the US believes that supporting the re-establishment of stability and adequate governance in Somalia represents the only sustainable long-term solution to piracy. This will require concentrated and coordinated assistance to states in the region to build their capacity to deal with the social, legal, economic and operational challenges to effective law enforcement.

While the focus on following ransom payments and using sophisticated law enforcement techniques to identify beneficiaries is seemingly positive, there are concerns that the US, along with other G8 members, is seeking to outlaw ransom payments.

The ban is aimed at terrorist groups but there are concerns that it will make it nigh on impossible to free seafarers if the Somali piracy plague emerges once again. It has been confirmed in several authoritative reports and by EUNAVFOR that no direct link exists between pirates and terrorists and researchers stress that piracy is a business model based on criminal activity, not terrorism.

In light of the emphasis on law enforcement, the IMO has also approved MSC.1/ Circ.1404 on guidelines to assist in the investigation of the crimes of piracy and armed robbery against ships, and adopted resolution MSC.324(89) on the implementation of BMP guidance.

# Arrest and prosecution

According to data from EUNAVFOR, the military in the Indian Ocean are forced to release around 30% of the pirates held near the coast of Somalia due to the difficulties in bringing them to justice.

The European Union currently has agreements with the Seychelles and Mauritius to transfer pirates. These transfer agreements are the result of complex negotiations that rely heavily on the measure of local politics and the EU requires standards in judicial and prison conditions.

The transfer of pirates to Seychelles or Mauritius occurs only as an alternative. According to the United Nations Convention on the Law of the Sea (UNCLOS), also known as the Convention of Jamaica, the country that imprisons a pirate has a preference for prosecuting that individual.

There is a second preference level, relating to the country of the attacked ship, flag or owner. However, countries often refuse to take the pirates arrested. In addition, seafarers are often unwilling or unable to travel to Seychelles or Mauritius to give evidence in proceedings.

# Catch and release

Despite prosecution being desirable, when the military cannot transfer the pirate to any country, all too often they are forced to release them.

The Spanish military often use the term "leave on the beach" to refer to this process. In reality, the release process usually sees the pirates allowed to leave custody near the coast, about 2km from land, in their own boats.

This is usually an area of their own tribe but as far as possible from any known pirate camps. When released, they are given enough food and water to perform the journey to shore but their outboard engines are often replaced with lesser powered units.

# West African Code

The Economic Community of West African States (ECOWAS), the Economic Community of Central African States (ECCAS) and the Gulf of Guinea Commission, pursuant to United Nations Security Council resolutions 2018(2011) and 2039(2012), have expressed concern about the threat that piracy and armed robbery at sea in the Gulf of Guinea poses to international navigation, security and the economic development of states in the region.

Accordingly, a comprehensive regional strategy and framework to counter piracy and armed robbery has been developed, including information sharing and operational coordination mechanisms in the region, building on existing initiatives such as those under the auspices of IMO.

Attacks have prompted pledges to combat piracy and maritime crime in coastal waters and ministers in a range of affected states have called for governments to arrest and prosecute suspected pirates and seize any vessels believed to have been used in acts of piracy.

Signatories to the Code intend to cooperate as fully as possible in preventing and repressing piracy and armed robbery against ships, transnational organised crime in the maritime domain, maritime terrorism, illegal, unreported and unregulated (IUU) fishing and other illegal activities at sea by:

- Sharing and reporting relevant information
- Interdicting ships and/or aircraft suspected of engaging in illegal activities at sea
- Ensuring that persons committing or attempting to commit illegal activities at sea are apprehended and prosecuted
- Facilitating proper care, treatment and repatriation for seafarers, fishermen, other shipboard personnel and passengers subject to illegal activities at sea, particularly those who have been subjected to violence

The IMO has reasserted its desire to assist western and central African countries to establishing a workable, regional mechanism of co-operation for enhanced maritime security.

Maritime development is an essential component of African development and maritime zone security is fundamentally important, requiring a genuine commitment from regional governments to tackle the problem.

There are some examples of this being done successfully and there are increasing demands for international support – financial, assets or people – to create, train and develop the capability of a military response force to tackle piracy and maritime crime across the region.

According to experts, communication is key and efforts should be channelled into creating a central source for information gathering and sharing. Once created, efforts must be made to counter under-reporting and ensure all shipping companies use this resource to maximise its effectiveness.

# Chapter 8
## The human element

### KEY ADVICE

- Understanding the effects of piracy on those attacked and their families
- Assessing campaigns to support and engage with seafarers
- Appreciating the importance of support and care for those attacked

The Djibouti Code of Conduct touches briefly on the issue of seafarer care and the need to support and assist crews that have been victims of piracy.

Issues such as physical injury and psychological trauma have to be taken seriously and every company should develop systems capable of dealing with the various stages of the aftermath.

The attack is simply the start of the experience; the struggle to deal with the legacy of their experiences and suffering can take much longer to heal. With the support of a structured approach, seafarers will be able to cope better and eventually put the pain, torment and suffering of captivity behind them.

## Seafarer support campaigns

**Save Our Seafarers** is one of the biggest ever maritime industry groupings comprising 25 of the world's largest maritime organisations. It was created to raise awareness of the human and economic cost of piracy and the rights to protection of innocent seafarers and the global economy.

The campaign is focused on compelling governments to take a firmer stance to help eradicate piracy, with a call for six key actions:

- Reducing the effectiveness of the easily identifiable mother ships
- Authorising naval forces to hold pirates and deliver them for prosecution and punishment

- Fully criminalising all acts of piracy and intent to commit piracy under national laws, in accordance with their mandatory duty to cooperate to suppress piracy under international conventions
- Increasing naval assets available in the affected areas
- Providing greater protection and support for seafarers
- Tracing and criminalising the organisers and financiers behind the criminal networks

The work of SOS has been scaled back and switched focus but it has clearly demonstrated the effect of public relations in forcing international action.

Another important campaign is the **Maritime Piracy Humanitarian Response Programme** which aims to fill an important gap in anti-piracy social service care. This covers:

**Awareness** – Ensuring that the number of hostages is not forgotten and providing a ready source of information on the scale of the problem

**Support** – A source of information on where and how seafarers who have suffered from attack or incarceration can access support, whether physical or psychological. This will also apply to the families, friends and colleagues of those who have been hijacked, or are still being held

**Information** – To act as a focal point for information on the human aspects of the issue. This will be in partnership with care agencies and the medical profession and will afford the press, media, companies and colleges with a trusted information partner

**Prevention** – Both campaigns look to disseminate best practice and feedback from partner organisations and supporters. The aim will be to raise awareness of the ways and means of avoiding capture but more so on dealing with the capture of hostages and coping afterwards

The ultimate aims are to ensure that seafarers are not forgotten and that those who suffer at the hands of pirates (whether seafarers or their family) will never have to guess at what resources are available to them or of the ways in which they can ease the physical or psychological scars to which piracy can lead.

# The end game

It may be possible to catch a hundred, even a thousand, young men who become the masked faces of piracy and punish them severely but the wheels of organised crime will still turn and more young men will be tempted into piracy. As a result, governments need to recognise the role they have to play in eradicating this sea-borne menace.

The real answer to the Somali piracy problem is as simple to appreciate as it is difficult to bring about. The long-term key is seen to be nation-building – to create community, life, careers, wealth and a sense of alternative pursuits for the young men so readily seduced into a life of piracy and violent crime.

While there is some progress in parts of the country, there are real concerns about the rule of law and a seeming distrust of the judicial process. The whole region is still seen as fragile, a tinderbox of potential conflict. It is to be hoped that investment and incentives can one day fill the void in which piracy has taken root. The elements that form the piracy triangle need to be broken apart but until then there is a genuine and terrifying threat to deal with.

The answers which have brought some signs of progress in the battle against Somali piracy could well be applied elsewhere – and fundamentally there is a need to tackle the economic drivers of crime, the weaponry which facilitates it and the underworld which thrives on it. Breaking the piracy triangle is vital – tackling conflict and poverty and creating laws which support progress rather than allowing pirates to avoid and evade capture are key. Off West Africa and around Asian pirate hotspots the issues are similar, but unique solutions will be needed there too.

While the wait for social and political solutions can take a long time – perhaps even generations – it has been seen that a combination of military action, private security capability and legal structure have brought positive results.

The navies massed in the Indian Ocean have reduced the spread and reach of pirates, while the protection afforded by having armed guards on ships have demoralised, frightened and deterred many attackers. Those who have been captured have been processed by courts and imprisoned.

Such progress is heartening, but still the embers of piracy can flare up. If complacency is allowed to creep in, if the military withdraws, or if the private security solution is dropped, then it would not take long for pirates to gain the upper hand.

It is also important that the best practice and lessons learned from such successes are exported and adopted elsewhere. For seafarers and the shipping industry, however, the solutions away from the vessel are beyond their control. For those reasons, the security of the vessel begins with the regime onboard and the support and resources afforded by the company.

Awareness, investment, support, intelligence, all add together to make ships a harder target – and ultimately the fight against piracy rests on these foundations.

# About the Author

## Steven Jones Msc Bsc (Hons) MNI

Steven Jones MSc BSc (Hons) MNI is Maritime Director of SAMI, the Security Association for the Maritime Industry. He spent a decade working as a navigation officer in the merchant navy and was attacked by pirates while serving. After moving ashore he advised numerous shipping companies on security planning – spending years researching, applying and developing an in-depth knowledge of security and the International Ship and Port Facility Security (ISPS) Code.

This knowledge has provided the basis for this publication and the main book in the maritime security suite, *Maritime Security: a practical guide* (published by The Nautical Institute in 2012), and other handbooks in this suite. He has also contributed articles to The Nautical Institute's magazine *Seaways* and other publications.

His primary focus is on the human element – particularly the ways and means of bringing security techniques and effective management to the attention of crews of merchant vessels, office personnel and ship operators. He has experience across the maritime industry, working for shipping companies, insurers, publishers and professional bodies. As well as SAMI he is the founder of the International Dynamic Positioning Operators Association (IDPOA). He is a Member of The Nautical Institute, the Chartered Institute of Public Relations and a Fellow of the Royal Society of Arts.

## More titles published by
## The Nautical Institute

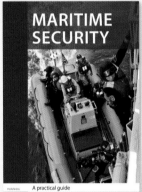

### MARITIME SECURITY

A practical guide

Steven Jones MSc BSc (Hons) MNI

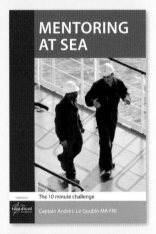

### MENTORING AT SEA

The 10 minute challenge

Captain André L Le Goubin MA FNI

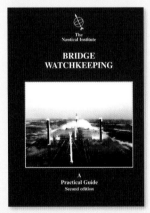

The Nautical Institute

BRIDGE WATCHKEEPING

A Practical Guide
Second edition

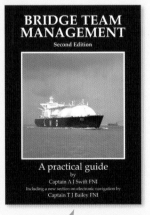

### BRIDGE TEAM MANAGEMENT
#### Second Edition

A practical guide
by
Captain A J Swift FNI
Including a new section on electronic navigation by
Captain T J Bailey FNI

The Nautical Institute